UMBRO
Conditioning
for
Football

UMBRO
Conditioning
for
Football

The total fitness programme for players of all levels.

Introduced by Alan Shearer

EBURY
PRESS

UMBRO

A TSL Publishing Limited Book

First published in Great Britain in 1997

1 3 5 7 9 10 8 6 4 2

Ebury Press
Random House, 20 Vauxhall Bridge Road, London SW1V 2SA

Random House Australia Pty Limited
20 Alfred Street, Milsons Point, Sydney, New South Wales 2061, Australia

Random House New Zealand Limited
18 Poland Road, Glenfield, Auckland 10, New Zealand

Random House South Africa (Pty) Limited
Endulini, 5A Jubilee Road, Parktown 2193, South Africa

Random House UK Limited Reg. No. 954009

A CIP catalogue record for this book is available from the British Library

ISBN 0 09 185405 9

Printed in Singapore

Papers used by Ebury Press are natural, recyclable products made from wood grown in sustainable forests.

This book was produced by TSL Publishing Limited
5, Peto Place, Regents Park
London, NW1 4DT
Tel: 0171 486 4446

Written by members of the staff from John Moores University

Designed by Melville & Melville

Contents

How can a football player develop speed, strength and endurance? How can a player prepare mentally for a match? What should a player eat and drink before, during and after a match or training session? How should a player plan, co-ordinate and monitor training throughout the year?

Umbro Conditioning for Football provides answers to questions like these. It explains the principles involved in preparing, physically and mentally, to play football.

Specific training exercises are included to improve flexibility, strength, speed and endurance, thus ensuring a player is conditioned to achieve peak performance. Information is provided on diet and nutrition, goal-setting, mental preparation, and planning your programme.

The book translates scientific principles into practical recommendations in a clear and easy-to-follow manner. It is essential reading for anyone who wants to improve their football, at every level of the game.

The authors

Liverpool John Moores University is at the forefront of applying science to football. Numerous research papers and books have been published as a result of studies conducted at the University and members of staff have been invited to act as counsellors to football associations in many countries as well as to professional clubs in the UK. The institution has made a unique contribution towards the scientific investigation of football and is renowned worldwide for its work.

The Centre for Sport and Exercise Science at the University offers the only academic course in the world which focuses on the application of science to furthering our understanding of football. The Diploma in Science and Football is a one-year full-time or two-year part-time course which requires students to study the theoretical underpinnings of football within a sports science framework. Areas studied include physiology of training; diet and nutrition; fitness testing and evaluation; injury prevention and rehabilitation; football violence; psychology of football; talent identification; management of players and club resources; computerised match-analysis; football strategy and tactics; biomechanics of football skills; playing surfaces and equipment. The Centre also provides opportunities for postgraduate study in science and football via the MSc Sports Science or the research awards of Research Diploma, M.Phil and Ph.D.

Further information can be obtained by writing to the Admissions Tutor, Centre for Sport and Exercise Science, School of Human Sciences, Liverpool John Moores University, Mountford Building, Byrom Street, Liverpool, L3 3AF, UK.

Mark Williams BSc (Hons), PhD: Senior lecturer in Sport and Exercise Science. Head of Science and Football at Liverpool John Moores University. Has considerable experience of conducting research in the area of science and football and has published several scientific papers on skill acquisition. A former schoolboy international footballer and an experienced football coach.

Andy Borrie BSc (Hons): Senior Lecturer in Sport and Exercise Science at Liverpool John Moores University. Over the last ten years he has worked extensively as a consultant exercise physiologist with several national sports squads. This work has included both fitness monitoring and training prescription.

Tim Cable BSc (Hons), PhD: Senior Lecturer in Sport and Exercise Science at Liverpool John Moores University. Has published extensively in the areas of thermoregulation and physiological adaptation to exercise. Has also been involved in fitness testing and injury rehabilitation with professional footballers both in the UK and Australia.

Dave Gilbourne BA (Hons), Cert Ed, MSc: Senior Lecturer in Sport and Exercise Science. Has published in the areas of mental preparation for performance and the psychology of injury and rehabilitation. Extensive experience of providing psychological support for professional footballers and other élite athletes.

Adrian Lees BSc (Hons), PGCE, PhD: Professor of Sports Science. Head of the Centre for Sport and Exercise Sciences at Liverpool John Moores University. Has contributed numerous scientific papers in the areas of biomechanical analysis, equipment testing, injury rehabilitation and strength training in football.

Don Maclaren Cert Ed, BSc, MSc, PhD: Principal Lecturer in Sport and Exercise Science at Liverpool John Moores University. Has researched in the area of sports nutrition for 16 years (especially on carbohydrates and ergogenic aids) and has advised many coaches and professional football players on nutritional support.

Thomas Reilly BA, Dip PE, MSc, PhD: Professor of Sports Science at Liverpool John Moores University. Director of the School of Human Sciences, Head of the University's Graduate School, Chair of the International Steering Group on Science and Football, Chair of the Exercise Physiology Steering Group of the British Olympic Association and former Chair of the British Association of Sport and Exercise Sciences. Has written four books and numerous scientific journal articles in the area of science and football.

The players

We would like to thank all those players and coaches who have contributed to the making of this book. We very much appreciate the support of Alan Shearer, Steve McManaman, Winston Bogarde, Roberto Carlos and Louis Van Gaal, both for their activities on the training ground but also for their insight into conditioning for football.

In particular we would like to thank Steve Payne who demonstrates many of the tests and exercises throughout the book. Steve is a semi professional player for Macclesfield Town.

Umbro Conditioning is a programme that could be the challenge of your life-time. If you follow the physical conditioning and motivational guidelines illustrated in this book, it could change you as an athlete.

There's no substitute for skill and technique. For the lucky ones, they are a gift. Usually they have to be won through sheer hard work. In order to reach the top, every sportsman and woman must have them.

Umbro Conditioning is for the individual. It is an approach that shows you how to achieve the potential you didn't know you had. With Umbro Conditioning, you will run those extra few yards when you can barely stand, and force yourself to do that extra press-up when your muscles scream "*No*". You will want to do the extra training because you know it will make you a better player on the pitch.

Umbro Conditioning won't make you a superstar overnight. Together with your skill and technique, it will give you the physical capacity and the will to get the best out of your talents — the perfect game plan.

The Umbro Conditioning for Football Book and Video will inspire you, the clothes will help you feel the part, but at the end of the day, it's up to you. The means are here — will you take up the challenge?

Alan Shearer

UMBRO
Conditioning
for
Football
VIDEO

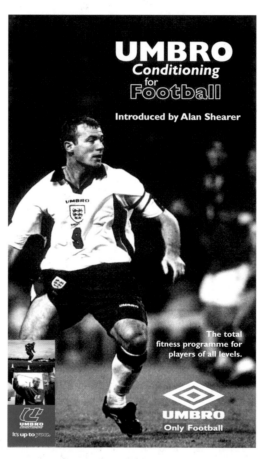

GOT THE BOOK, NOW GET THE VIDEO…

PACKED WITH EXCITING FOOTAGE FROM EURO 96, THE PREMIER LEAGUE AND INTERNATIONAL GAMES
THIS 60 MINUTE VIDEO FEATURES ALAN SHEARER, STEVE MACMANAMAN, WINSTON BOGARDE,
ROBERTO CARLOS, LOUIS VAN GAAL AND STEVE PAYNE DEMONSTRATING THE CONDITIONING EXERCISES
AND DISCUSSING THE VITAL IMPORTANCE OF CONDITIONING IN THEIR FOOTBALL CAREERS.

TO ACHIEVE THE POTENTIAL YOU DIDN'T KNOW YOU HAD.

UMBRO CONDITIONING FOR FOOTBALL.

IT'S UP TO YOU.

AVAILABLE FROM BRITAIN'S MAJOR VIDEO RETAILERS.

FOR FURTHER INFORMATION CALL

THE GAME ENTERAINMENT GROUP

01608 652475

Aerobic **and** *Anaerobic* conditioning

Football is the total sport. Footballers are a combination of sprinters and marathon runners; they must perform with short bursts of power and speed, but also have the ability to keep going for ninety minutes or more.

"There have got to be times, when you're going to have to make 30 or 40, maybe even 50-odd runs, during a game. So physical fitness is very, very important."

Alan Shearer

To be successful, players must train to increase both their speed and endurance.

The actual distance that a player covers during a game depends on playing position, team tactics and style of play, but at the final whistle, an outfield player may have travelled up to 13 km (8 miles).

How the outfield player spends his/her 90 minutes:

- 18–27 mins   (20-30%)   Walking
- 27–36 mins   (30-40%)   Jogging
- 13–23 mins   (15-25%)   Running
- 9–13 mins   (10-15%)   Sprinting
- 4–7 mins   (4-8%)   Walking backwards

All this varied movement needs energy to drive the muscles of the body, particularly the legs. Energy is supplied by a special chemical (ATP) that is stored within the muscles themselves. Unfortunately the amount of ATP stored within the muscle is limited to just one second's supply, enough to perform a single shot at goal, a single jump or a single tackle.

The reason players can keep moving for ninety minutes is that the ATP used is immediately replenished. This rebuilding of energy happens in a number of different ways depending on the activity of the player. For example, if a player is sprinting, then ATP will be rebuilt using the anaerobic energy system; in a player who is jogging or walking, ATP will be rebuilt using the aerobic energy system.

Note: The relationship between aerobic and anaerobic energy is NOT divided precisely. Rather it is progressive with some purely aerobic activities (walking) and some purely anaerobic activities (jumping to head a ball, rapid sprint over 5 metres/yards). Most activities fall at some point along this continuum and involve some interaction between the two.

Anaerobic Energy System

The anaerobic energy system works during sprinting or fast running which may last for 1–30 seconds.

- During these times, oxygen is not available to produce energy and therefore ATP is renewed by breaking down carbohydrates stored in the muscle. Although energy is produced very quickly, a substance called lactic acid is also produced which causes fatigue and muscle tiredness.

- Players can tolerate or avoid fatigue by performing anaerobic training. This consists of two components: speed training and speed endurance training.

So the aims of anaerobic training are
- To improve speed and power.
- To increase the player's ability to maintain speed and power for longer during a game.
- To increase the body's ability to recover after heavy exercise.

The benefits of anaerobic training to a player will be faster acceleration, more energy and a quicker removal of lactic acid, which will cause less fatigue and improve the recovery time after sprinting.

"When you saw Pele play, Tostao playing, Rivelino playing, they played practically with the ball at their feet. Nowadays, no. Nowadays, when you leave your marker position, you've got to be physically fit to get from one end of the field to the other."

Roberto Carlos

Aerobic Energy System

The aerobic energy system is used to fuel endurance activities of a lower intensity, such as walking, jogging or running at slow to moderate speeds and is used to provide endurance. This system produces energy by supplying oxygen to the muscles. Oxygen delivery is increased by training the heart and cardiovascular system to pump blood more effectively around the body.

So the aims of aerobic training are:

- To help the body carry oxygen more effectively.

- To increase the ability of the muscle to use oxygen.

- To increase the body's ability to recover after high intensity exercise.

The benefits after a period of aerobic training will be a significant increase in the delivery of oxygen to the exercising muscle, the muscle will be better adapted to use oxygen, and there will be less of a build-up of lactic acid during exercise, and therefore less chance of fatigue.

As a player only sprints for about half a mile (850 m) during a match, much of the energy supplied comes from the aerobic system – but even though aerobic energy production is more common, it is the sprinting activity that often means the difference between winning and losing.

It is therefore very important for players to undertake both aerobic and anaerobic training.

"When I first came into the game at 11, we'd never even heard of fitness coaches, but we had one at Blackburn and we have one at Newcastle...they're coming into the game more and more now." Alan Shearer

How to improve your aerobic and anaerobic condition

Before you start any conditioning it is important to memorize a few key guidelines. All good programmes are based upon five important principles:

- **Overload** Training must be sufficiently strenuous to overload the system that is being trained.

- **Progression** As your fitness improves it takes a higher level of exercise stress to make you even fitter.

- **Specific** Training has to be specific to a particular aspect of conditioning. If you want to develop sprinting speed then use anaerobic training *not* aerobic training.

- **Reversibility** All training effects are reversible. Remember "Use it or lose it".

- **Recovery** Remember to allow adequate rest after training. It is during this time that the body adapts to training.

Measuring the effect of training

Before embarking on any training programme, it is essential to establish your level of fitness so that you can:

- monitor your rate of progress

- set training goals

- remain motivated.

Measuring aerobic capacity

Working out your maximum oxygen consumption reveals your aerobic capacity and level of endurance.

In this test you must attempt to run as far as possible in exactly 12 minutes. The test can easily be performed by running around a football pitch as long as the dimensions are known (the distance could be paced out if no measure is available). The formula used to calculate aerobic capacity is 0.0225 x metres covered minus 11.3 (0.0206 x yards covered minus 11.3). So if you run 3000 metres in 12 minutes, your capacity is 56.2 units. Put into context, the average professional midfield player ranks at 62.4 units.

	Full-back	Centre-back	Midfield player	Striker	Goalkeeper
Professional player	62	56	62	60	51
Semi-professional player	Typical value for a defender 55		58	54	N/A

Table 1: Average aerobic capacity for different playing positions for professional and semi-professional players

Measuring anaerobic capacity

30 metre (33 yard) sprint test

Stand between two cones placed about 1 metre (1 yard) apart. From a standing start, on the count of two, one, go, sprint to a set of cones located 30 metres (33 yards) down field. The time taken from the instruction "go" to crossing the cones should be recorded.

This test measures your ability to respond to a signal and accelerate to maximum speed. It reflects your potential for rapid energy production and therefore power. Any time under 5 seconds is a good one, with professionals averaging 4.0 seconds.

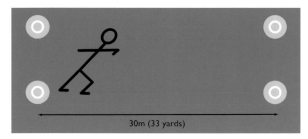

30m (33 yards)

Sprint/fatigue test

On the command two, one, go, sprint from A to B, deviating sideways by 5 metres (5.5 yards) in the middle of the sprint (see page 24, Figure 2). The time from "go" to crossing the cones at B should be recorded. After crossing the cones, jog a further 10 metres (10.95 yards), round the final cones and back to the start point, taking approximately 30 seconds to get from B back to the start. As soon as you arrive back at the start, you should then sprint to B again. This cycle of events is therefore repeated once every 30 seconds. In total this is repeated seven times, with the sprint time between A and B recorded each time. The difference between fastest and slowest times reflects your ability to recover between sprints. The sideways deviation includes a component of agility into the test.

This test gives you results such as:

Sprint						
1	2	3	4	5	6	7
Time (seconds)						
6.73	6.88	7.01	7.14	7.35	7.50	7.65
Fatigue time (slowest – fastest)						
7.65 – 6.73 = 0.92 seconds						

Time (seconds)	Best	Mean	Fatigue
Average	6.80	7.10	0.64
Range	6.53–7.01	6.83–7.31	0.15– 0.92

Table 2: Typical values for professional football players

Testing yourself on a regular basis allows you to see the real benefit of your aerobic and anaerobic training programme. Setting and achieving personal goals – like reducing the fatigue time in the last test – can provide real enjoyment and satisfaction.

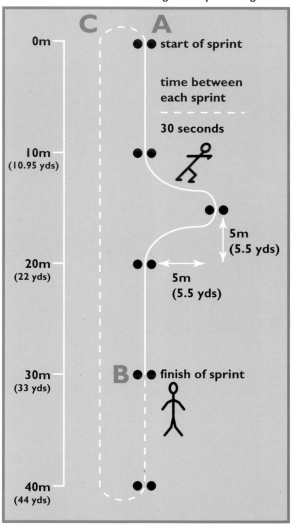

Figure 2: Sprint/fatigue test

C A

0m — ● ● start of sprint

time between each sprint

30 seconds

10m (10.95 yds) — ● ●

20m (22 yds) — ● ●

5m (5.5 yds)

5m (5.5 yds)

30m (33 yds) — B ● ● finish of sprint

40m (44 yds) — ● ●

Aerobic Training

Aerobic training can be achieved using:

- **continuous training** (work without rest at a moderate intensity e.g. jogging). This type of training is suitable for pre-season work.

or

- **intermittent interval training** (work at high intensities separated by periods of rest or easier work). This type of training is more suited to late pre-season and in-season training.

Monitoring training

As you go along, it is important to monitor your progress by measuring **heart rate**. This will ensure that you are working hard enough and will tell you how your fitness is improving. Heart rate is best measured by placing two fingers on the radial artery (which can be found in the wrist just below the base of the thumb). Alternatively, heart rate **(HR)** can be measured at the carotid artery in the neck (the finger should just rest lightly on the neck). Count the number of beats in 15 seconds and multiply by 4 to give the pulse rate in beats per minute.

Heart rate in training is usually lower than maximum heart rate which is calculated **as 220 minus the person's age.** For example, a 20-year-old player has an estimated maximum heart rate of 200 beats per minute. If the desired intensity of exercise is 80% of that, then the target heart rate will be 160 beats per minute.

Types of training

1. Low intensity aerobic training

(i.e. early pre-season at approximately 80% of maxiumum heart rate)

This usually involves continuous jogging for at least 20–30 minutes three times per week. One of these sessions could include what is known as Fartlek training. This form of exercise involves running and walking at different speeds for 30–45 minutes. For example, a player may jog slowly for a couple of minutes, run at three-quarter pace for a minute and then walk to recover, before starting the cycle all over again.

2. High intensity aerobic training

(i.e. late pre-season and in-season at approximately 90% of maximum heart rate)

This usually involves interval training, i.e. short bursts of high activity separated by periods of lower intensity exercise and rest. The rest and recovery periods allow the work intensity during exercise to be higher than during continuous training.

See Table 3 below for an example of high intensity aerobic training.

It is important to note that the purpose of interval training is not to run yourself to exhaustion on the first repetition. The idea should be to run all repetitions at the same even pace. If you've paced your session correctly, the last repetition should be hard but you should be able to complete it without slowing down excessively at the end.

Your best time for 3 miles continuous running is 19 minutes 30 seconds

It would be pointless for you to try to achieve a pace of 6 minutes per mile for 3 miles (i.e. 3 miles in 18 minutes). However, you should be able to sustain that pace for half a mile, completing it in 3 minutes. This could be built into an interval session as follows:

Interval session	Repetitions	Distance	Target time
	6 x	½ mile in	3 minutes

Total distance covered = 3 miles. Time taken for total distance = 18 minutes

On completing this session you should have run 3 miles in 18 minutes, something which you would not have been able to do with continuous running.

Table 3: High intensity aerobic training

Here are some other ideas for interval training

Progressive lap

Start in the lower left corner of the pitch, jog around three sides of the pitch until you reach the lower left corner and then run at three-quarter pace, along the goal-line back to the start (see Figure 3 below). Repeat immediately, but this time jog along two and a half sides of the pitch followed by a three-quarter pace run from the halfway line back to the start (i.e. one and a half sides of the pitch). Repeat, jogging to the diagonal corner followed by a three-quarter pace run back to the start (i.e. two sides of the pitch). Continue in this manner increasing the run (three-quarter pace) by a half side of the pitch until an entire lap is completed at three-quarter pace.

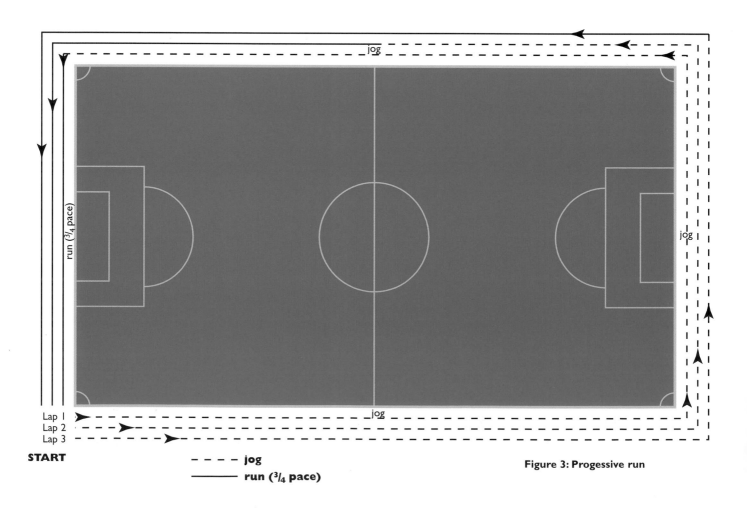

Lap 1
Lap 2
Lap 3

START

- - - - **jog**
———— **run (³/₄ pace)**

Figure 3: Progessive run

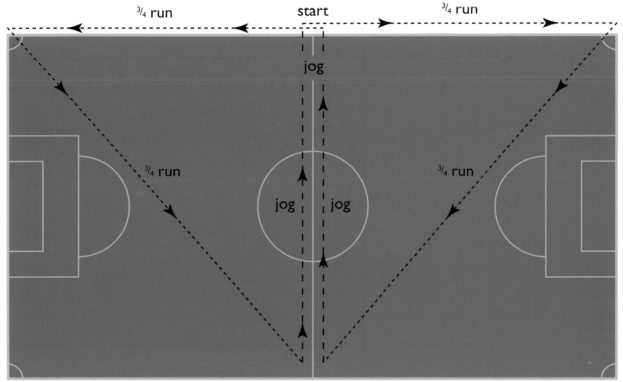

Figure 4: Diagonal running

The next three exercises should be performed at around three-quarter pace

Diagonal running

Start at the halfway line, run along the sideline to the corner flag; turn and run diagonally across the pitch to the junction of the halfway line and sideline. Jog along the halfway line as a recovery (see Figure 4 above). Repeat using the other half of the pitch. Repeat 3–5 times for 2–3 sets.

Half pitch interval run

Run from one goal-line to the halfway line, return and repeat immediately. This should take approximately 30 seconds and be followed by one minute's recovery (during pre-season). Recovery should be active: either ball juggle or jog slowly around the penalty area. During the season, the recovery period should be reduced to 45 seconds and then 30 seconds as fitness improves. Repeat the whole process 3–5 times per set; try to complete 2–3 sets.

Penalty area run

Start in the corner of the box and the goal-line; run along the goal-line. At the next corner of the box, jump to head an imaginary ball, land and side-step up to the 18 yard line. Run backwards across the top of the box, and then side-step down the remaining side (leading with the other leg). Continue for 1 minute and recover for 2 minutes (pre-season) and 90–60 seconds mid-season. Repeat 3–5 times for 2–3 sets.

3. Recovery training

(usually at 65% of maximum heart rate)

This type of training should be undertaken the day after a match or a particularly hard training session, in order to help the recovery process. Coupled with flexibility exercises, it can help prevent the muscle soreness players commonly experience at this time. A slow recovery jog should normally be for 20 minutes at heart rate levels of 110–130 beats per minute.

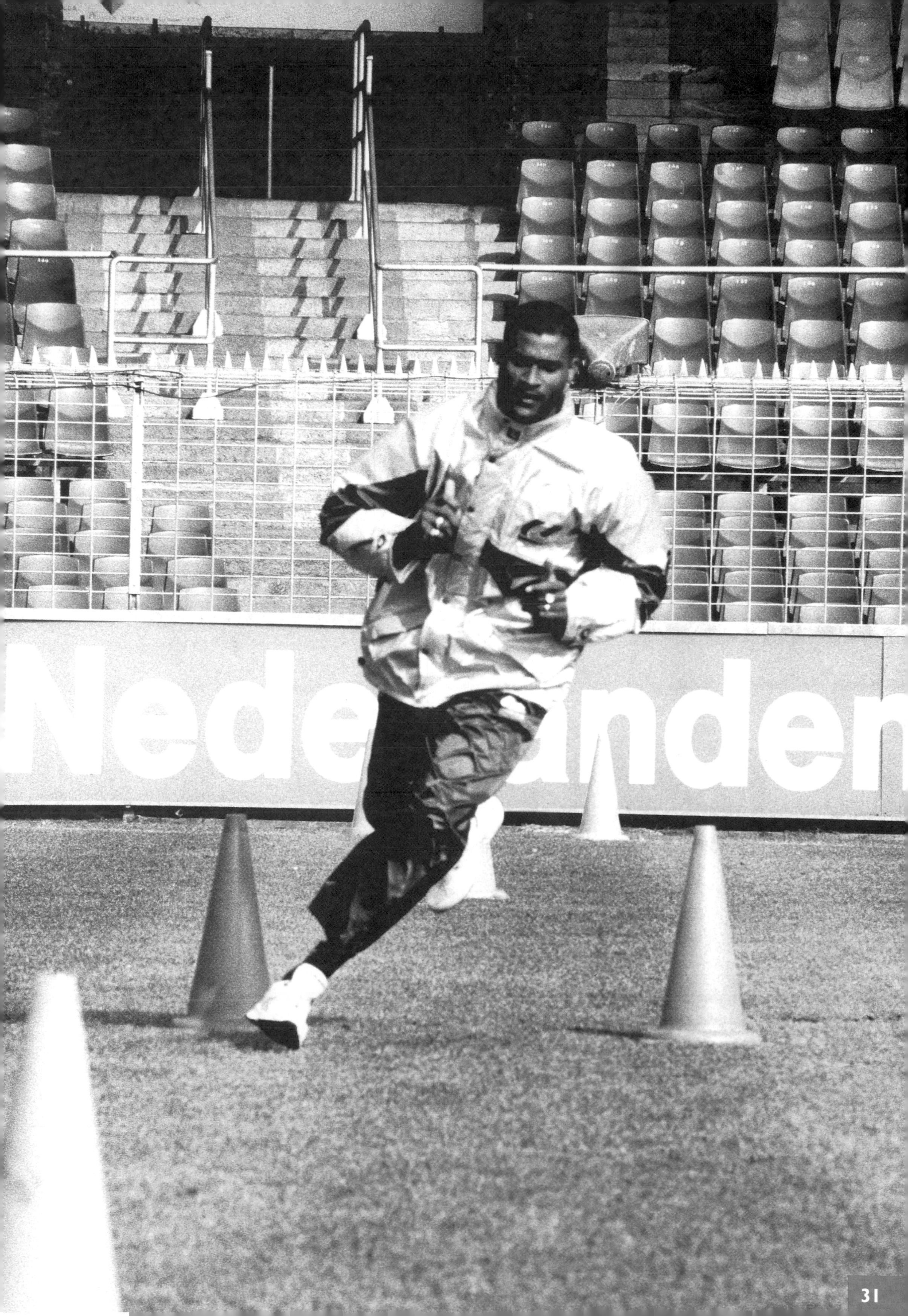
Nede anden

Figure 5: Stepping-striding exercise

Anaerobic Training

This consists of speed training to improve the anaerobic energy system and speed endurance work to increase the removal of lactic acid, thus reducing the recovery times after high intensity exercise.

Types of training

1. Speed training

It is important to improve speed off the mark as well as your acceleration when already moving. This can be achieved by concentrating on the power of the first few strides, and the speed of leg movement. Consequently, this type of training is only performed over short distances. Ideally, sprint training should be undertaken alongside, or after, a strength and power conditioning programme.

Basic repetition sprints

A typical workload for a speed-training session should be approximately 5 sets of 10 repetitions. Ten second sprints should be followed by 50 second rests to ensure quality is maintained (i.e. the work to rest ratio should be around 1:5).

Examples of speed exercises

Stepping-striding exercise

Place some markers in a straight line on the ground about a metre/yard apart for a total of 10 metres (11 yds). From a standing start, run the length of the markers, taking one stride between each marker, as fast as possible. With practice, move the markers closer together to encourage faster and shorter strides (see Figure 5). Repeat 10 times. A progression can involve going from short-stride running to longer strides for the next 10 metres (11 yds), followed by regular sprinting for 10 metres (11 yds). Such exercises are useful since players have to alter their stride length continually during a game.

Standing start

From a standing start, accelerate as quickly as possible over 10–20 metres (11–22 yds). You can vary this by doing some other activity just before the sprint (e.g. start from kneeling or lying, pretend to jump for a header, pretend to receive a ball and lay off a pass, or make a sharp turn). Try to make the starts as realistic/match-like as possible.
See Figures 6, 7, 8 and 9.

Figure 6:
Standing
starts

Running start

As before, but you should already be moving before you start to sprint e.g. start with a 5 metre (5.5 yards) jog before exploding into a sprint or jog backwards for 5 metres (5.5 yards), turn and explode into the sprint.

Figure 7: Standing start sprint

Hill sprint

You can make each sprint harder by using an incline or bank of about 30 degrees. This helps to work on the power you can generate during the crucial first few strides. Explode up the hill for 10–20 metres (11–22 yards), then walk slowly back down for recovery. It is important to note that since hill sprints are harder you may need to allow a slightly longer recovery period in order to maintain quality.

Downhill sprint

From standing, sprint downhill for 10 metres/yards. The hill should be *very slight*. This works on the speed of leg movement, *not* on how you generate power. You will find that since your legs are working far faster than in an uphill sprint, this helps to improve the co-ordination of the legs when sprinting.

The following drills take slightly longer for each repetition and therefore the recovery period should also be increased. Also, you may wish to reduce the number of repetitions in each set (e.g. 3 sets of 6–8 repetitions).

Hollow sprint

Sprint over 30 metres/yards, jog 30 metres/yards, sprint over 30 metres/yards, jog 30 metres/yards. Walk/jog back to starting point for recovery.

Cruise and sprint

From the goal-line, gradually accelerate to reach top speed at the halfway line and sprint to the far 18 yard line. Stop, turn and walk/jog back to the starting point as part of your recovery. This is similar to hollow sprints except that in this sprint you progressively build up to top speed.

Figure 8: A variation on the standing
start using the pushing over of the cone
to signify the control of a ball
(i.e. lay-off) just before the sprint

2. Speed endurance training

Speed endurance training allows a player to sustain a very high work intensity for longer. In order to achieve these two training effects

- You must be working flat out, or very near it. This is vital to improve anaerobic energy production.

- The duration of each repetition of a drill should last between 30 seconds and 2 minutes. The emphasis is on improving your ability to keep sprinting and enhancing your recovery from such exercise. It is therefore important to adhere as closely as possible to each drill's exercise and recovery time.

Hollow sprint

Sprint and jog as before; slow down to a walk, turn and repeat immediately (this should cover the length of the pitch). Keep repeating this sequence for 2 minutes, then take 2 minutes gentle jog recovery. A total of 6–8 repetitions (1 repetition = 2 minutes work) should be a good session.

Cruise and sprint

As before, from the goal-line gradually accelerate to reach top speed at the halfway line and sprint to the far 18 yard line. Slow down gradually, turn and repeat the sequence. Keep repeating this sequence for 2 minutes, then take 2 minutes gentle jog recovery. A total of 6–8 repetitions should be a good session.

Fast penalty sprint

Sprint from goal-line to 6 yard line and back, penalty spot and back, 18 yard line and back, edge of the D and back. Do as much as possible in 60 seconds followed by 60 seconds recovery. Repeat 3–5 times per set with 2–3 sets per session.

Continuous sprint

Sprint diagonally across the penalty area for 60 seconds followed by 60 seconds recovery. Repeat 3–5 times per set with 2–3 sets per session.

Note: The number of sets and repetitions highlighted in this chapter are only intended as a guideline. You can vary your training by undertaking a range of exercises in each session.
For example, a 20–30 minute speed endurance training session could include 8 repetitions of the hollow sprint or 4 cruise and sprint and 4 hollow sprint repetitions, or 2 sets of 5 repetitions on the fast penalty sprints and continuous sprints respectively. Similarly, a speed training exercise could have a lower number of repetitions on a range of speed drills. The actual structure of your training session will depend on the duration and objectives of the session and on current fitness levels (see chapter on planning your programme, page 87). **However, it is important to vary your training to maintain interest.**

Penalty spot run

Start on the penalty spot. Sprint to one corner of the penalty box then back to the start, followed by a sprint to the next corner of the box and back (see Figure 10). Continue until you have completed one circuit of the penalty box then rest for 60 seconds. Repeat 5 times per set with 3–4 sets per session.

Figure 10: Penalty spot run

Figure 9: Standing start sprints

As Alan Shearer says, when asked to give young players his advice on fitness and conditioning:

"Always enjoy it…at the end of the day, if you don't enjoy it, then you'll struggle. Push yourself hard but not too hard, and know when you've done enough, but the most important thing is that you enjoy it."

Strength
conditioning

"You've got to be strong enough to hold a defender off behind you who wants to nick the ball off you."

Alan Shearer

Strength Conditioning

Muscle strength is vital for footballers

- **Lower body strength** is required in movements such as tackling, jumping, kicking, starting and stopping, turning and changing speed.

- **Upper body strength** is required for resisting tackles, throwing-in, heading a ball and for goalkeepers when catching a cross.

"You've got to do weight work. The stronger you can be, that's all the better. You've got to be in fine condition, so you've got to do it regularly."
Alan Shearer

Strength conditioning with the use of weights increases basic muscle strength, muscle endurance and, most importantly, explosive power i.e. the ability to apply muscle strength very quickly.

Improved **muscle strength** increases overall playing performance and reduces the risk of injury.

Improved **muscle endurance**, or stamina, helps to keep your performance high despite working very hard for intense periods during the game.

Improved explosive power helps you to perform rapid movements such as jumping, sprinting and turning more effectively.

"Nowadays, you use your physical strength more than your skill, so if you're physically fit on the field, you can beat your opponent."
Roberto Carlos

Training techniques
Isometric The contraction of muscle when the muscle length itself does not change.

Concentric The contraction of muscle when the muscle length is shortened; for example, conventional resistance strength training using free weights or a weights system.

Eccentric (also known as plyometric)
The contraction of muscle when the muscle is trying to shorten but its length actually increases. This increases explosive power.

"Maintaining the level of physical fitness happens in the weight room with an individual programme."
Louis Van Gaal

"If you play three games in one week, it's impossible to train your legs, so you can only maintain the upper part of your body."

Louis Van Gaal

Basics of Weight Training

Picking the correct weight

The table below will help you to choose the right weight for your own training programme, whether it be to develop muscular strength, power or endurance.

Repetitons (RM Load)	3	6	12	-->	-->	20	25
Loads (% of 1 RM max)		95-90%	85%	70%	-->	-->	60%	50%
	STRENGTH	STRENGTH	STRENGTH			Strength	
	POWER	POWER	POWER			Power	
	Endurance	ENDURANCE		ENDURANCE	ENDURANCE	
	Maximal Strength	<--	Maximal Power	<-- TO -->		Endurance	

Table 4: The varying size of the lettering in this table indicates the levels of benefits for either strength, power or endurance. The higher loads with fewer repetitions develop strength. Endurance is developed with 50% of your maximum load but 25 repetitions

---

RM Load or Repetition Maximums.

This is defined as "the heaviest weight that you can lift a given number of times". For example, if you can only lift the bench press once at a certain weight, that is a 1RM; if you can lift a lower weight twice that is 2RM and so on.

When should strength training be done?

Muscle strengthening exercises are best used out of season, about 2–3 times per week, when basic muscle strength is most usefully developed.

As the season approaches, concentrate on developing both muscular endurance and power. Basic muscle strength training should be maintained,

but given lower priority during the playing season, reduced to perhaps one session per week. In any case, at least 48 hours should be left between strength training and playing in a match to avoid muscle fatigue.

Warm up

Always warm up before you start – it prepares you for the coming exercises as well as helping to avoid the risk of injury and the effects of muscle soreness. Make sure you warm up all of the muscles. Before lifting a very heavy load or performing a strenuous exercise, do some practice movements.

Check your progress

Re-evaluate the load lifted every 6–8 weeks. This can vary depending on how comfortable you feel. You will only get better if you put the work in.

In the early stages of training, strength gains are more noticeable and there may be a small increase in the load lifted every 2 weeks. You should keep a record of the exercises, loads lifted and number of repetitions.

Order of exercises

- Always exercise the large muscle groups (e.g. legs, back, chest) first because the small muscle groups (e.g. arms, shoulders) will tire as the training sessions progress.

- Always alternate arm exercises with leg exercises to allow the maximum amount of time for the muscles to recover.

- Always vary exercises during a weekly schedule to give muscles a chance to recover fully from previous training. For example, work some upper body muscles one day and other upper body muscles the next.

Basic Muscle Strength Conditioning

- Use low speed movements.
- All muscle contractions should be performed with maximum effort.
- Keep the load at about 5RM.
- Increase the weight as you get stronger.
- For each exercise, complete 2–4 sets comprising 5 repetitions per set with 2–5 second rest periods between repetitions.
- Allow several minutes between sets.

start phase (first 4 weeks of closed-season)		
first week	1-2 sessions	2 sets per session
second week	1-2 sessions	2-3 sets per sessions
third week	2-3 sessions	3 sets per session
fourth week	3 sessions	3 sets per session
training phase (early pre-season)		
	3 sessions	3 sets per session per week
maintenance phase (late pre-season and in-season)		
per week	1-2 sessions	2-3 sets per session

Table 5: Example of general structure of a weight-training programme

Training exercises

Most of these exercises can also be carried out using free weights.

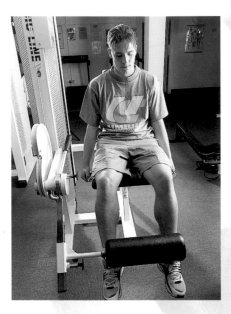

Quadriceps (thigh) muscles – leg extension
Adopt a comfortable position in the leg extension machine. Begin with the legs in a flexed position. Extend slowly until they reach maximum position, hold this position briefly, then slowly flex the legs again, under control, until they reach the start position.

Calf muscles – standing calf raises
Stand upright and hold the weight across the shoulders. Push up on to the toes and slowly return to a normal standing position.

Hamstring muscles – leg curl
Adopt a comfortable position in the leg curl machine. Begin with the legs extended, flex and slowly return to the starting position.

Front and side stomach muscles

Lie on your back on the floor with the legs held at the ankles. Hold the ball behind your head. Lift the upper body and then return to the starting position. Alternatively, during the flexion phase turn the upper body alternately from left to right to work the side abdominal muscles.

Upper back muscles

Sit with your back straight. Pull the bar down to your neck and slowly return it to the starting position.

Leg adductor (groin) muscles

Stand upright, place a ball between your legs and press inwards to compress the ball. Hold for 20–30 seconds. Do three sets of 3–5 repetitions.

Chest and arm extension muscles

Sitting bench press

Slowly push the bar forwards until your arms are fully extended. Bring the bar back towards your chest in a controlled fashion.

Arm flexion muscles – biceps curl

Sit in a comfortable position resting your arms on the pads. Turn the palms of the hands upwards. Lift the weight towards the chest and lower slowly.

Lying bench press

Lie face up on a horizontal bench with the weight to be lifted supported in a weight rack or by a travel limiter.

Hold the bar at arm's length using a medium width grip so that your hands are about 15–20 cm (5–8 in) wider than your shoulders.

Wrap your hands completely around the bar and slowly lower it so that it gently touches the chest. Do not attempt to bounce the bar off the chest.

"Slowly" push the bar upwards until your arms are fully extended again above the shoulders.

Throughout the movement, your head and buttocks should remain in contact with the bench, your back should be straight and your feet should be firmly placed on the ground.

Shoulder muscles – shoulder press

Sit in a comfortable position with your back flat against the chair. Lift the bar above your head until your arms are fully extended, then slowly lower them.

Muscular Endurance Conditioning

- In general, lower weights and higher repetitions are used.

- The load used should be half of 5RM.

- For each exercise, complete 2–4 sets with at least 15–20 repetitions per set.

- Push yourself. Increase the load once 15–20 repetitions can be lifted comfortably.

- Allow 1–2 minutes between sets.

Muscular endurance can be achieved without using free weights or a multi gym system. The exercises that follow involve the use of body weight only.

These can be incorporated into what is generally called a circuit-training programme.

Circuit training is based on the same principles as the interval training sessions described on pages 25–29. Typically, you work hard at an exercise for 30–60 seconds then rest for 30–60 seconds.

Designing a suitable circuit-training programme

- Don't work the same muscle groups in successive exercises. For example, alternate between upper body, leg and stomach muscle groups.

- Perform one set (e.g. 30–60 seconds) for each exercise then move on to the next exercise.

- Do 3–5 sets for each exercise.

- Training intensity should be increased progressively by increasing the exercise period for example from 30 to 60 seconds and/or by reducing the duration of the recovery period (e.g. from 60 to 30 seconds).

▷ 6A   **7**   ▷ 7A   **8**   ▷ 8A

KODAK 5053 TMY   13   KODAK 5053 TMY   14   KODAK 5053 TMY

▷ 12A   **13**   ▷ 13A   **14**   ▷ 14A

KODAK 5053 TMY   19   KODAK 5053 TMY   20   KODAK 5053 TMY

▷ 18A   **19**   ▷ 19A   **20**   ▷ 20A

KODAK 5053 TMY   25   KODAK 5053 TMY   26   KODAK 5053 TMY

▷ 24A   **25**   ▷ 25A   **26**   ▷ 26A

▷ 9A   10   ▷ 10A   11   ▷ 11A

KODAK 5053 TMY   16   KODAK 5053 TMY   17   KODAK 5053 TMY

▷ 15A   16   ▷ 16A   17   ▷ 17A

KODAK 5053 TMY   22   KODAK 5053 TMY   23   KODAK 5053 TMY

▷ 21A   22   ▷ 22A   23   ▷ 23A

KODAK 5053 TMY   28   KODAK 5053 TMY   29   KODAK 5053 TMY

▷ 27A   28   ▷ 28A   29   ▷ 29A

Basic muscular endurance exercises

Front abdominal muscles – sit-ups

Lie on your back with your hands behind your neck
and knees bent with your feet on the floor. Lift your
body so that your elbows touch your bent knees.

Front abdominal muscles

This is an alternative to sit-ups. Lie on your back
with your hands behind your neck. Lift your legs and
knees off the ground and at the same time lift your
upper body off the ground. The knees/legs should be
permanently off the ground whilst you lift your
upper body each repetition.

Side abdominal muscles

Another alternative to sit-ups. Lie on your back with
your hands behind your neck. Lift your legs and
knees off the ground and at the same time lift your
upper body off the ground turning alternately to the
left and right, touching each knee with your elbow.

Side abdominal muscles

Lie on your back with your hands behind your neck
and knees bent with your feet under a fixed ledge
or held. Lift your head and trunk so that your
elbows touch your bent knees alternately on the left
and right. The knees/legs should be permanently off
the ground whilst you lift your upper body each
repetition.

Back muscles

Lie on your stomach. Extend your arms to arch the back. Hold the position for 5 seconds and then lower.

Back muscles

Lie on your stomach. Lift your upper body off the floor. Hold the position for 5 seconds and then lower. As a further progression, lie on your stomach. Lift one arm and the opposite leg at the same time. Alternate with the other arm and leg.

Chest and arm muscles – press-ups

Face down, support your body with fully extended arms. Bend your arms to lower your head and chest towards the floor. When your chest is just above floor level, push up to complete the movement.

Leg muscles 1

Using a step or a low bench, step on and off it as quickly as possible leading with right and left leg alternately.

Leg muscles 2

Alternatively, starting from a standing position on top of the bench, straddle the bench with both feet then bounce back up to the start position as quickly as possible.

Arm muscles – triceps dips

Using a bench or a chair, place your hands on the edge of the bench as if you were about to push off from a sitting position. At the same time, stretch your legs out in front of the bench. Bend your elbows until your backside is almost touching the floor; then extend your arms to complete the movement. Keep your elbows close to your sides during the exercise.

Leg muscles – squat thrusts

Start in the normal press-up position, face down with arms fully extended. Bring your knees up to your elbows in a jumping movement, then fully extend your legs.

Explosive Power Conditioning

- Generally, moderate weights and faster repetitions are used.

- Use moderate weights and lift explosively, i.e. move the weight as fast as possible during the initial stage of the lift.

- The load used should be approximately 10RM.

- For each exercise, 2–4 sets should be completed, with 8–10 repetitions in each set.

Plyometrics (rebound or eccentric muscle training)

This is the most effective way of improving power. It involves rapidly stretching muscles and storing the energy in an elastic part of the muscle. When the muscle contracts and shortens the stored energy is used. Plyometric conditioning helps the body to store and use energy. You should use fast, powerful reactive movements immediately after a muscle has been stretched and the muscle must be stretched rapidly, not slowly.

For example, in plyometric jumping exercises, when you land you should explode upwards again as soon as you feel your feet touch the floor. You should *not* try to sink right down into a deep squat and then jump as high as possible. The objective is to minimize ground contact time between jumps.

Guidelines for plyometric training

You must develop a well-balanced strength base before undertaking a high volume of plyometric training. Bad preparation increases the risk and reduces the benefits to be gained. Always warm up, concentrating on the thigh, calf and lower back region. Do 5–10 minutes of jogging and/or skipping followed by 5–10 minutes stretching. For more details on warm-up, see page 97.

- Plyometric training will not leave you out of breath or feeling tired so beware of overdoing it early in a programme. This will result in severe muscle soreness 24–48 hours later. Stick to your programme regardless of whether you feel it is too easy at the start.

- All actions should be performed using maximum speed, effort and technique. The intensity of each exercise has to be sufficient to ensure overload.

- Adequate rest is vital between exercise sequences. Two minutes between sets is normal.

- Generally, two sessions of plyometrics per week, allowing at least 48 hours recovery in-between, is enough.

- Most exercises are done in sets of 8–10 repetitions but adjust accordingly. If technique starts to deteriorate, a set should be stopped.

- 3–6 sets per session are suitable for intense jumping drills (e.g. plyometric jump running and bounding).

- 6–10 sets are suitable for less intense skipping and hopping work (e.g. plyometric drop jumps and raise jumps).

- A session should never contain more than 120 explosive ground contacts for any muscle group.

- Increase work-rate intensity progressively.

- If muscle soreness develops, end the session immediately.

When should plyometrics be done?

Over a year: A year's programme is aimed at bridging the gap between strength and power as well as improving acceleration and jumping ability.

The exercises should be done after a period of strength conditioning. They should be introduced midway through pre-season training and continue during the season.

Over a week: You should not do a hard session the day before a match. Muscle performance can suffer for several days after a hard plyometric session.

Over a session: These exercises should come at the start of your training session when your muscles are fresh and can produce the explosive movements required.

Sessions should end if there are signs of tiredness such as reduced vertical height in jumps and loss of co-ordination of arms and legs.

Equipment

Running shoes with some kind of shock absorbing
heel are best. Hard surfaces such as concrete are
not recommended; a flooring with some kind of give

Basic plyometric and explosive power exercises

Split squats

Start in a split-squat position.

Drive into the air reversing the position of the legs before landing, so if the left leg was in the front the right is in front on landing.

Jump back to the start position and repeat the sequence the required number of times.

Plyometric jump running

Use a slow speed running action landing on alternate feet but try to gain as much height as you can during the airborne phase of each stride.

Plyometric bounding

Make a series of forward jumps, landing and taking off from both feet, jumping as far and as high as you can. Increase the difficulty by placing obstacles in the way which you then have to bound over. Remember, try and minimize ground contact time. These jumping movements should be performed rapidly.

Lateral jumps

Stand next to a bench or small obstacle and jump sideways with both feet as high over the obstacle as you can. Jump back to the start position. Repeat for the required number of jumps.

Plyometric drop jumps

Step off a bench or box on to a firm (but not concrete) surface and rapidly jump vertically as high as you can.

The height of the bench or box will depend on the level of training; it should be about 30 cm (12 in) but may be lower to start with. Increase difficulty by increasing the height of the drop.

Explosive power jumps

Take a short run on to a box, about 30 cm (12 in) high, landing with one foot on the box, and then jump off powerfully, pushing off with the same leg and reaching as great a height as possible.

While in the air, practise heading an imaginary ball.

Skips

Alternate hop–step exercises with emphasis on both height and horizontal distance.

Ricochets

Mark a small box shape on the ground. Move both feet from one corner of the box to the other in a random manner. Place emphasis on rapid rate of leg and foot movement rather than height or horizontal distance.

"I often look to see if I've improved...to see if the work in the week has been worthwhile. I think if you practise hard and work hard, then it will come."

So says Alan Shearer, assessing his own training progress.

Measurement of Strength

Assessing progress

In order to check your progress, you should keep a training diary including details of your training programme and a record of fitness test results.

The measurement tests described below require maximum effort and it is essential to undertake a thorough warm-up before starting.

Tests employing free weights should always be performed with a partner, never alone.

Basic muscle strength

This can be assessed using a one repetition maximum (1RM) of the basic strength training exercises (e.g. bench press and leg press).

The use of a weights machine (rather than free weights) is recommended, for safety reasons.

Measurements of basic strength should be made relative to body weight; the score is a fraction of body weight lifted. For example, if a player whose weight is 80 kg (176 lb) can leg press 140 kg (308½ lb), then the score is 140/80 = 1.75.

Example Score Sheet			
Name: John Smith		Body weight: 74 kg	
	Load lifted (kg)	Score	Rating
Bench press	65	$^{65}/_{74}$ = 0.88	**
Leg press	150	$^{150}/_{74}$ = 2.02	****

Bench press	Poor *	**	***	****	Excellent *****
Men	0.6	0.8	1.0	1.2	1.4
Women	0.3	0.4	0.5	0.6	0.7
Leg press	Poor *	**	***	****	Excellent *****
Men	1.4	1.8	2.0	2.4	2.8
Women	1.2	1.4	1.8	2.0	2.2

Table 6: Assessing basic muscle strength

Muscular endurance

This can assessed by determining how many repetitions of an exercise can be performed in a set time, e.g. 60 seconds. Sit-ups and press-ups are good exercises to use, but any of the endurance exercises described could be used instead.

The score is the number of complete repetitions achieved in one minute.

Sit-ups	Poor *	**	***	****	Excellent *****
Men	20	30	40	50	60
Women	20	30	40	50	60
Press-ups	Poor *	**	***	****	Excellent *****
Men	10	20	30	40	50
Women (* modified)	10	20	30	40	50

Table 7: Typical values for professional and semi-professional players
* Press-ups using a bent knee support i.e. weight on the knees rather than on the feet.

Measurement of muscular power – standing vertical jump

Explosive power may be assessed using the following test:

Stand on a firm surface close to a vertical wall. In a side-on position, stretch up with the hand closest to the wall and chalk a mark on the wall. Return your hand to your side and, using your arms to swing upwards, jump as far up the wall as you can. Chalk a mark as high as possible on the wall. The score is the difference between the baseline mark and the highest mark on the wall.

Standing Vertical Jump Test					
	Poor *	**	***	****	Excellent *****
Men (cm)	46	49	52	55	58
Women (cm)	36	39	42	45	48

Competitive level	Standing Vertical Jump Height (cm)
Professional	60
Semi-professional	54

Table 8: Typical values for professional and semi-professional players carrying out the standing vertical jump

Standing vertical jump test

Flexibility conditioning

Flexibility Conditioning

Flexibility is the range of motion at a joint or joints and is unique to each joint. It can be improved by exercises which stretch the soft tissue (muscles and tendons) surrounding each joint.

Stretching is often used as part of a warm-up, but it has an important role beyond this. Flexibility training is beneficial for enhancing performance and also to prevent injuries.

However, despite its importance, research shows that over two-thirds of professional footballers have poorer flexibility than other athletes. Flexibility training must be included in all training programmes and should be given a high priority throughout the year.

Benefits of Flexibility Training

1. Performance enhancement

Flexibility training can:

- Lead to a greater range of motion in the joints which allows for more reach when needed (e.g. stretching for a ball or a tackle).

- Lead to greater muscle force in rebound movements such as jumping and sprinting.

- Enable muscles to apply force over a greater range of motion of the joint, so that the muscle can do more work and generate greater speed (e.g. increasing the power of kicking).

2. Injury prevention

Flexibility training can help prevent injury by decreasing the incidence, intensity and duration of musclo-tendonous injuries. Specifically, it can:

- Increase the range of motion of a joint and avoid muscle tightness. Therefore muscles are less likely to tear or become strained at the limit of their range (e.g. in a follow through after a kick, sprinting, and when stretching to make a tackle).

- Increase the elastic strength of muscles and tendons. This enables the muscle and tendon to stretch more easily during forced extensions (e.g. tackling) and to withstand impact.

- Relieve muscle soreness after intense exercise.

- Promote muscle relaxation to prevent muscle tightness.

- Help the recovery process after muscle injury along with physiotherapy and an appropriate strength rehabilitation programme.

How to stretch

When you perform a stretching exercise, move slowly to the limit of your range, just before the point of discomfort. Always use slow movements and don't bounce. Consciously stretch the target muscle, and hold the stretch for 10–30 seconds.

This easy stretch reduces tension, maintains flexibility and improves circulation. The feeling of the stretch should diminish as the stretch is held. If it intensifies or becomes painful, you are overstretching and should stop. The only way to tell if you are stretching correctly or overstretching is by the feeling of the stretch. It's important to get used to the feeling and to listen to what your body is telling you.

After the easy stretch you can move further into the stretch until a mild increase in tension is felt. This is the development stretch. Hold this for about 10–30 seconds. The feeling of tension should either decrease or stay the same. Any increase in tension is a sign of overstretching and you should ease off slightly. The development stretch further reduces tension and increases flexibility and may be repeated for greater effect.

Stretching and warm-up

Before you stretch, warm-up (see page 97). A warm-up helps warm and relax the muscles, helping the stretching process.

Light stretching should be included in any warm-up routine because it helps to increase circulation and prepare muscles and tendons for exercise (see section on planning, page 87). However, this light stretching used to exercise muscles gently and mobilize joints during a warm-up shouldn't be confused with the stretching used as part of flexibility training. Stretching as part of flexibility training is designed to increase the flexibility of muscles and tendons over and above their current levels.

Football's demands mean that lower body and trunk muscles are likely to need most attention. An exercise programme which emphasizes stretching of hamstrings, calf muscles, groin, back, quads and shoulders will be of most benefit.

Flexibility programme

Key points:

Preparation	Warm-up to relax muscles and improve circulation.
Specifics	Each joint and muscle group needs to be isolated and treated separately; therefore a range of exercises is needed.
Duration	10–30 seconds for each stretch, performed slowly.
Repetition	1–3 repetitions each exercise.
Frequency	Once per day if possible but at least 3 times per week and always before a training session or match.

Achilles and soleus stretch

From calf stretch position, slightly bend the back knee, keeping foot flat. This gives a lower stretch which is good for ankle flexibility.

Suitable exercises for footballers:

Calf stretch

Bend one leg in front of you leaving the other leg straight behind, foot flat on the ground. Move your hips forward slowly until you feel a stretch in the calf of the straight leg. Keep the heel of the straight leg on the ground and toes pointed straight ahead.

Squat (groin)

Place feet shoulder-width apart and pointed slightly outwards with your heels on the ground. Bend your knees and squat down with your hands on the ground in front of you. Push your knees outwards with your elbows to stretch the groin muscles. But be careful if you have a knee injury.

Sitting hamstring stretch

Sit upright with the leg to be stretched extended and flat on the floor. Bend the other leg and put the sole of your foot close to the thigh of the extended leg. Lean forward slowly from the waist while extending both hands to grip the ankle. The extended leg should be kept straight, with the toes pointed towards you, at all times. Repeat, then stretch the other leg in the same way.

Alternatively, in the same position, lean forward slowly as far as possible from the waist without bending your back.

Lying flex stretch

Lying on your back, pull your left leg towards your chest, keeping the back of your head on the ground. Repeat with the other leg.

Standing quads

Standing on your right leg, bend your left leg. Hold the top of your left foot with your left hand and gently pull the heel towards the buttock. Repeat with the other leg.

Standing hamstring stretch

Place the ball of your foot on a secure surface just above knee height, keeping the other leg straight. Bend the knee of the support leg as you move your hips forward. Repeat with the other leg.

Sitting quads

Sit with one leg flexed and close to the buttocks. Bend the other leg and place the sole of the foot close to the other knee. Slowly lean back using your hands to support your trunk. Repeat with the other leg.

Sitting groin stretch

Sit upright, flex thighs and legs and bring the soles of the feet together. Grip your legs slightly above the ankles and rest your elbows on the inside of the thighs above the knees. Use the elbows to push your thighs slowly towards the floor.

Sprinter's stretch

Move one leg forward until the knee is directly over the ankle. Rest your other knee on the floor. Lower the front of your hip downward without changing the position of the knee on the floor. Repeat with the other leg.

Lying groin

Relax with knees bent, the soles of your feet together and as close to the groin as possible.

Standing groin
Point feet straight ahead and more than shoulder-width apart. Bend your right knee slowly and move your left hip down towards the right knee, thus producing a stretch in the right inner thigh. Repeat with the other leg.

Rotational trunk stretch
Stand with your feet slightly apart. Turn your hips as you look behind, over your shoulder. (see trunk rotation test on page 76).

Lateral trunk stretch
Legs slightly apart, grip your elbows above your head. Slowly bend sideways from the waist pulling the elbows behind your head at same time. Do not bend forward at the waist. Repeat on the other side.

Lying trunk stretch
Lying on your back with arms spread out, bring your right leg with the knee slightly bent over your body towards your left hand. Repeat with the left leg.

Measuring flexibility

The following three tests are to assess flexibility. To check your progress, you should do all three tests and record your scores every 6–8 weeks.

Pull head forward

Lying on your back, place your hands behind your neck and bring your head, neck and shoulders forward until you feel a slight stretch.

Modified sit and reach test

This test measures hamstring and lower back flexibility.

Equipment required

I metre (36 in) tape measure or rule, box.

Sit on the floor with buttocks, shoulders and head in contact with a wall. Extend your legs with knees straight and the soles of your feet placed against a box approximately 30 cm (12 in) high. Place your hands together, with neither set of fingers extending beyond the other.

Place the measure on top of the box with the zero end pointed towards you. Reach as far forward as possible without allowing your head or shoulders to come away from the wall. The rule must be held so that the zero end touches your extended fingers. This has now set the zero point, or bench mark for this test. It's important that this yardstick is held firmly in place until the test is complete.

Overhead stretch

In a standing position, interlace your fingers above your head, palms up. Push your arms and hands back and up.

Now lean forward slowly, allowing your head, shoulders and trunk to move away from the wall and your fingers to slide along the top of the yardstick, making sure the yardstick does not move. Make three slow forward movements, and on the third, move forward as far as possible holding the position for two seconds. Read off the distance your fingers have moved along the rule. Record your best score from three separate attempts. You are measuring the difference between the benchmark and your maximum reach.

Modified sit and reach test		
poor	average	excellent
15cm (6 in) 25cm (10 in) 30cm (12 in) 35cm (14 in) 45cm (18 in)		

Table 9: Modified sit and reach test

Trunk rotation test

To assess pelvis, trunk and shoulder flexibility.

Equipment required: tape measure or rule.

Mark a vertical line on the wall. Stand upright, facing away from the wall with feet slightly spread apart, straddling the line. You should be about 50 cm (20 in), or an arm's length, away from the wall. Twist your trunk to the left and touch the wall with the fingertips of both hands at shoulder level. Record the distance of your right fingers from the vertical line when twisting left. The fingers crossing the line to your right gives a positive value.

Repeat in the opposite direction with a twist to the right and measure the distance of your left fingertips from the vertical line. The fingers crossing the line to the left gives a positive value. The final score is the average of the left and right scores.

Trunk rotation test		
poor	average	excellent
0	5 cm (2 in) 10 cm (4 in) 15 cm (6 in)	20 cm (8 in)

Table 10: Trunk rotational test

Groin flexibility test

Equipment required: tape measure or rule.

Sit on the floor with your knees apart and the soles of your feet together. Place your hands on your feet and slowly bring your feet towards the groin, keeping your knees as close to the floor as possible. The score is the measured distance from groin to heels.

Groin flexibility test		
poor	average	excellent
25 cm(10 in) 20 cm(8 in) 15 cm(6 in) 10 cm(4 in) 5 cm(2 in)		

Table 11: Groin flexibility test

Goal-setting **and** conditioning

"It is very important to set goals. As a coach you have experience with setting goals for the players individually and you hope that the efforts will become visible on the field."

Louis Van Gaal

A player must strive to achieve targets; attaining them leads to an increase in self-confidence and can enhance motivation. They focus attention on specific aspects of personal development and allow the individual to single out areas of improvement.

Establishing and linking goals

When devising goal-setting programmes, it is useful to strike a balance between short-term and long-term goals.

Long-term goals

It might be helpful to see longer term goals as the end of the journey. For example, you may form the long-term goal of playing for your country, or playing professionally. Once long-term goals have been established, it is important to consider what has to be done to get there. Once you have decided that, the specific or day-to-day content of the goal-setting programme will start to emerge.

Short-term goals

These relate to specific areas of improvement and can be set on a daily or weekly basis. Achieving such goals gives a sense of satisfaction. Progress is being made and that provides a spur to go further.

The successful attainment of short-term goals leads to the fulfilment of the long-term goal.

When Alan Shearer suffered a serious injury a few years ago, his long-term goal was to get back to full fitness. He achieved this by creating a programme of specific short-term goals:

"I did a lot of running, a lot of pounding up and down the steps to get into a fine condition and lots of stretches to strengthen up the quads and hamstrings to help support the knee."

Alan Shearer

Sometimes it is helpful to picture the link between short-term and long-term goals as a staircase, with the long-term goal located at the top. The stairs in-between represent short-term goals; these are equivalent to a series of intermediate steps that must be attained before the final goal is realized. Climbing the "goal staircase" requires a great deal of effort, simply setting goals will not in itself lead to progress. For a player's game to develop, goals must be committed to and acted upon, and for even the most gifted players this means hard work in

"No-one ever has been, really, the finished article. There's always something someone can improve on, and I'm no different."

Alan Shearer

training.

Linking goals together

Divide each goal into action steps. These should be specific, realistic and challenging. For example:

Long-term goal: To establish a first-team place.

Intermediate goal: To start the season as a physically stronger player.

Short-term goal 1: To improve leg and upper body muscle strength.

  Action step 1: Organize a weight-training programme.

  Action step 2: Complete calf, quadriceps and hamstring circuits on Tuesdays and Fridays.

  Action step 3: Complete chest, shoulder and back circuits on Mondays and Thursdays.

Short-term goal 2: To increase explosive power in legs.

  Action step 1: Organize plyometric training programme.

  Action step 2: Complete plyometric training sessions on Monday and Thursday.

The intermediate goal is a target for the start of the season while the long-term goal is a flexible

target to achieve first-team status at some time during the season. The short-term goal is more specific and is linked to the daily action steps.

Such an approach could be used to develop any aspect of conditioning such as flexibility, mental preparation or speed endurance. Setting goals in all these areas may be important in assisiting the player to achieve the long-term goal of establishing a first-team place.

Task and ego goals

Goals are sometimes referred to as task-type or ego-type goals. Task goals encourage players to assess how their game is now compared to, say, last season. For example, they might review if they are any faster or stronger than last year. In contrast, ego-type goals result in players assessing progress by

> - **Task goals** – used to compare scores against previous scores for the same task or test.
> - **Ego goals** – used to assess progress against other players.

evaluating their speed or strength against that of other players. When setting goals it is helpful to use ego-type and task-type goals together.

A task-only goal programme makes no allowance for comparison with other players. In a football team, measuring yourself against others can be an invaluable and natural process.

Be careful, however, because comparing your performance against other players can have a negative effect on self-confidence. Use any comparisons in a positive manner.

For example, observation of a successful player's strength on the ball may lead to a long-term ego-type goal to become stronger to overcome competition for the first-team place. This in turn leads to a short-term task-type goal which is to devise and commit to a personal weight-training programme.

Competition goals

Setting targets can also focus your energy during a match. Goals that are set during competition have also been classified as process or outcome in nature. Outcome goals reflect a teams desire to win or to keep oppositions scoring chances to a minimum. Process goals focus on what has to be done to make outcome goals a reality.

> - **Process goals** – used to help individual performance e.g. "getting forward to support the attack" or "keeping things simple early in a game".
> - **Outcome goals** – used to reflect the team's common objective e.g. winning the game.

Although setting outcome goals is a natural part of the game, always bear in mind that these goals are more difficult to achieve than process goals because they can be influenced by factors outside the individual's control, such as a bad refereeing decision or a bad injury to a key player. So it is better for a player to concentrate on realistic process goals before a match. Process goals are more personally orientated and focus your attention on the things you want to do well during the match.

"You should never place the bar at a higher level than you can achieve because if the distance between goal and reality is too great, the player will not be able to cope."

Louis Van Gaal

"If you set goals too far ahead and you fall behind then it's a big big disappointment. Push yourself hard but the most important thing is to enjoy it."

Alan Shearer

Goal-setting in practice

Some important points to bear in mind when setting goals and assessing progress:

- Goals must present a challenge so that they really do provide a test.

- They must be realistic. There is little point in setting yourself a goal which is beyond your capabilities. It is important to believe that the goal is attainable.

- They must be stated in positive terms (i.e. things to achieve rather than things to avoid).

- Write them down so that you have a structured record of your goals.

- Goals should aim to highlight areas of weakness and maintain areas of strength.

- Keep a record of progress and include all relevant information. If things are going well, consider new targets. If things are going badly, consider why progress has not taken place; it might be necessary to set more realistic goals.

Finally, although developing a personal programme is invaluable, it is also possible for goal-setting to be a negative process if it is carried out incorrectly. Try to keep to the guidelines set out here.

Weekly Goal-setting Diary

Short-term goals for the week ahead

	Action steps	Thoughts on the session

MONDAY

TUESDAY

WEDNESDAY

THURSDAY

FRIDAY

SATURDAY

SUNDAY

Evaluation of the week's training

Planning **your** conditioning programme

You should aim to devise an efficient and effective training and conditioning programme individually tailored to your needs. Time spent doing this can save you problems later on. Think about what you want to achieve in soccer and what fitness standards that will entail.

Take stock

What is your current standard of fitness? What time and facilities do you have at your disposal?

Be realistic

There is little point in devising a plan which you will be unable to keep to. If time is limited, prioritize your fitness goals. Decide which aspects of conditioning (strength, flexibility, stamina, speed, power) require most attention.

A conditioning programme is only as good as the total amount of work you put in to it. **Failing to plan is planning to fail.**

"We're all different sizes, some are stronger and some are quicker."
Alan Shearer

The Annual Plan

Effective conditioning is not achieved overnight. It is a gradual process and one which builds up over several months.

Divide the annual plan into three categories:
– **Closed season**
– **Pre-season**
– **In-season**

This allows you to co-ordinate the different types of conditioning that you need to do, so that you can achieve the best performances at critical moments during the season.

Closed Season	Pre-season		In-season
Active Recovery	General all-round endurance	Start to develop football specific endurance	Maintain football specific endurance

Table 12: How aerobic conditioning should progress through a programme

Closed Season	Pre-season		In-season
Active Recovery	General all-round strength build-up	Develop maximum strength	Start to develop maximum muscle endurance, maintain strength conditioning and power

Table 13: How strength conditioning should progress through a programme

"At Internazionale, we had a specific routine which ran the entire year and by the end of the championship you were 100% physically fit."

Roberto Carlos

Conditioning for different parts of the season

1. Closed-season effective conditioning

Professional footballers know that once the season is over, it is not a signal to abandon all physical exercise. The result of doing only very limited amounts of physical conditioning will be a marked decline in personal fitness levels.

Remaining active during the close season, even at a reduced rate, maintains fitness. You want to ensure that time is not wasted later on regaining last year's fitness level.

However you do need to use this time to concentrate on mental and physical recovery. It will help you avoid becoming mentally stale and decrease susceptibility to injury.

Even Louis Van Gaal, one of the strictest disciplinarians in the game admits:

> *"When I see that they are overtired, I send the players on a holiday."*
> Louis Van Gaal

Maintain fitness through non-football related activities such as swimming, tennis and cycling. As a guide, try to do any activity that raises the heart rate to approximately 140 beats per minute for 20–30 minutes two or three times per week.

Such activities provide a mental break from the game whilst helping to maintain reasonable conditioning levels.

2. Pre-season effective conditioning

The longer the pre-season programme, the better the fitness level is likely to be when the season starts.

As a guide, the typical duration is between 8 and 12 weeks. If necessary, break down the conditioning programme into early and late pre-season. This enables you to alter the balance of your conditioning as you move from the start to the end of your pre-season conditioning period.

Over this period the type of conditioning should change from general to football specific conditioning.

> *"Pre-season is the time to get fit. By the time you get to February, March and April, you're just keeping yourself ticking over."*
> Alan Shearer

Month	June	July	Aug	Sept	Oct	Nov	Dec	Jan	Feb	Mar	Apr	May
Phase	CS	EPS	LPS	IS	IS	IS	IS	IS	IS	IS	IS	IS or CS
			COMPETITION								

Table 14: Annual plan for a football player
Key: CS – closed season (active recovery), EPS – early pre-season, LPS – late pre-season, IS – in-season

> *"When I'm in Brazil I try and keep fit as much as possible during the closed season. For a footballer this is very important because you always have to keep in trim so you can go back to the club fit."*
> Roberto Carlos

"Pre-season's just to get you back into the running and fitness of the game. At Liverpool, we normally have about two weeks running getting your fitness levels back up."

Steve McManaman

3. Early pre-season conditioning – back to basics

Do not place yourself under intense strain at this early stage. It is as important to know when to rest as it is when to work.

Concentrate, instead, on preparing yourself for the high-intensity conditioning which will be a feature of the later stages of the programme.

Aerobic and anaerobic endurance

Allow 1–2 weeks of continuous exercise to ease back into conditioning. You need to be hitting the exercise intensities for continuous exercise outlined on page 25.

Aim to increase the distance covered, or the length of time you are exercising, from session to session.

After this inital period, begin to focus on interval conditioning for endurance work, and bringing in the soccer specific interval sessions outlined on page 25–29.

You should aim to increase the speed of your runs rather than their length, whilst still keeping to a minimum of 20–30 minutes each run.

Strength, power and speed

The basis for the development of power and speed is general strength conditioning. Developing maximum strength takes at least 8–12 weeks of conditioning. If strength is an especially high priority, consider starting during the closed season. Although the closed season should be a time for rest, this does not exclude developing general strength.

> **"Speed cannot only be developed in the weight room, but also, and especially on the field, by giving them speed exercises."**
> Louis Van Gaal

Regardless of when you start your strength training, you should initially focus on all-round body conditioning exercises. This should be followed by heavier weights to maximize muscular strength after around 2 weeks of general conditioning.

If you are conditioning using weights, the correct combination of repetitions and sets for increasing maximal strength is given on page 44.

> **"With Ajax we play a lot of games and you must listen to your body and work out where you need extra training."**
> Winston Bogarde

Conditioning type	Pre-season programme conditioning priority		In-season
	First 4 weeks	**Second 4 weeks**	
Aerobic endurance	High -------> Low	Low -> Maintenance -> Low	Low (Maintenance only)
Aerobic/Anaerobic endur.	Low -------> High	High -------> Mod	Mod (Maintenance only)
Strength	High -------> Mod	Mod -------> Low	Low (Maintenance only)
Power	Low -------> Mod	Mod -------> High	Mod (Maintenance only)
Speed training	Low -------> Mod	Mod -------> High	Mod (Maintenance only)

Table 15: Priority ratings in an 8 week pre-season programme

Conditioning type	Pre-season programme conditioning priority			In-season
	First 4 weeks	Second 4 weeks	Third 4 weeks	
Aerobic endurance	High ----> Mod	High ----> Mod	Maintenance	Low (Maintenance only)
Aerobic/Anaerobic endur.	Low ----> Mod	High ----> Mod	Mod ----> Mod	Mod (Maintenance only)
Strength	High ----> High	Mod ----> Mod	Low ----> Low	Low (Maintenance only)
Power	None ----> Low	Mod ----> High	High ----> High	Mod (Maintenance only)
Speed training	None ----> Low	Mod ----> High	High ----> High	Mod (Maintenance only)

Table 16: Priority ratings in a 12 week pre-season programme

4. Late pre-season conditioning – quality rather than quantity

In this phase, your conditioning becomes far more soccer related with the emphasis on high-intensity conditioning. As the intensity of conditioning goes up, you will find that the length of each training session comes down.

Aerobic and anaerobic endurance

At this stage, focus on developing endurance through high density interval training and soccer-related speed endurance exercises.

Strength, power and speed

Move on to power and endurance exercises using circuit conditioning and plyometrics (appropriate repetitions and sets are given on page 46).

This bridges the gap between the strength conditioning that was undertaken during the closed and early pre-season periods, and the speed and power that you require during a match. Introduce soccer-related speed work.

Summary of priorities in pre-season training

Tables 15 and 16 are guides. Your own programme will depend on your individual needs and goals.

5. In-season conditioning

The emphasis here should be on maintaining the fitness levels built up during pre-season. Particular emphasis should be placed on maintaining aerobic/anaerobic endurance through interval training and speed and power via plyometric and speed exercises.

Weekly conditioning principles

- Establish a coherent weekly plan incorporating all the principles outlined here.

- The need for adequate rest and recovery periods remains a priority. During periods of recovery, the body responds to conditioning.

- Avoid exposure to a very high physical demand on consecutive days.

- When conditioning sessions which focus on different components of fitness follow each other, it isn't necessary to wait for complete recovery.

- Sessions which require high quality and/or intensity should not be undertaken when the body is fatigued.

- General aerobic or anaerobic endurance doesn't require the same kind of quality as speed or power conditioning. For example, in Table 17 if the midweek match is easy, high-intensity interval work can be done in the session on Thursday.

- Structure your session carefully. Where there is a split focus, for instance improving aerobic endurance and sprinting speed, the conditioning demanding the highest quality of work (i.e. sprint training) must come first.

The following examples of weekly training schedules should help your planning.

	Monday	**Tuesday**	**Wednesday**	**Thursday**	**Friday**	**Saturday**	**Sunday**
Training effort	Hard	Light/Rest	Moderate	Hard	Rest	Match	Light
Example session	Plyometrics 90-120 ground contacts -- REST -- 30-45 mins aerobic/ anaerobic endurance (e.g. diagonal running, progessive lap, fast penalty sprints)	Speed drills 5 sets of 10 reps 20-30m sprints	Weights (whole body session) focusing on muscle strength and/or endurance Flexibility training	**Split session** Plyometrics 90-120 ground contacts -- REST -- 30-45 mins aerobic/ speed endurance (e.g. hollow sprints, penalty spot run, fast penalty sprints)		**P R A C T I C E M A T C H**	Aerobic 20 mins gentle jog to aid recovery. Flexibility training.

Table 17: Late pre-season training with a practice match on the Saturday. A similar balance of sessions, in terms of training effort, could be used in-season when you have one match per week

	Monday	**Tuesday**	**Wednesday**	**Thursday**	**Friday**	**Saturday**	**Sunday**
Training effort	Hard	Light/Rest	Moderate	Moderate	Rest	Match	Light
Example session	Plyometrics 90-120 ground contacts -- REST -- 30-45 mins anaerobic/ speed endurance work (e.g. cruise and sprint, continuous sprint, penalty spot run)	Flexibility training	**M A T C H**	*(If it was an easy match)* **Split session** Repetition speed/sprint drills 4 sets of 10 reps + 20-30 mins aerobic/ anaerobic endurance (e.g. diagonal running, cruise and sprint) Half pitch drill 3 sets of 3 reps Flexibility training *(If it was a harder match)* Fartlek 25 minutes Flexibility training		**M A T C H**	Aerobic 20 mins gentle jog to aid recovery. Flexibility training.

Table 17: In-season training with two matches, Wednesday and Saturday

"You have to warm up before a game. Before you start any kind of training you have to be in very good technical and physical shape."

Roberto Carlos

Warm-up

An effective warm-up results in:

- **Increased performance**
  Muscles can produce energy much faster when they are warm.

- **Decreased risk of injury**
  A cold muscle is quite stiff and rigid which means that the muscle finds it difficult to contract quickly. Sudden forceful movements may create more tension than a muscle can control resulting in a muscular strain.

A good warm-up routine can also provide an opportunity to practise key skills and enables players to focus mentally on the upcoming exercise.

Key questions on warm-up

How long should a warm-up be?

The muscles take about 10 minutes to reach a steady temperature, therefore your warm-up should be at least this long. However, it can vary depending on the weather – it takes a shorter time on a hot day and longer on a cold day.

A resting muscle will never be warmed up whatever the temperature, so you should always perform some warm-up exercises. It can help to wear protective clothing during warm-up.

Muscle temperature reduces rapidly when the exercise is stopped. If you do a 15 minute warm-up 20–30 minutes before kick-off, the benefits gained during the warm-up may be lost by the time the match starts. If the break is short (e.g. five minutes), the loss in muscle temperature can be regained by performing some exercises on the field immediately before kick-off.

What intensity should warm-up be?

Exercise intensity at the start of the warm-up should initially be low, increasing gradually as the warm-up progresses. Final exercise intensity during warm-up should match the intensity of the match or training.

The first exercises should use the larger muscle

groups in the body without any explosive or sudden movements. Once the muscle has been warmed up slightly in this way, you should go through a light stretching routine (see section on flexibility, page 67).

Initially hold these stretches for a relatively short time period (i.e. 5–10 seconds). As your warm-up progresses, the duration of each stretch can be increased (i.e. 10–15 seconds).

Since the stretching exercises are merely used to help warm-up the muscles, the stretch is held for a shorter time period than during flexibility (see section on flexibility, page 67).

Afterwards, the intensity of the warm-up can be increased gradually. Further stretching exercises should be undertaken before any high-intensity activities.

What activities can I do in warm-up?

You should try and do part of the warm-up on your own. This may also be an ideal time to use imagery or mental rehearsal (see section on mental preparation, page 109) in order to help prepare psychologically for the match.

An important part of the pre-match warm-up should involve some work with a ball so that you have a feel for the ball and pitch prior to the match.

Whatever tasks you choose should be technically easy in order to maintain exercise intensity at a high level. If you keep stopping and starting you will lose the physical value of the warm-up.

Strike a balance within the warm-up between individual and team activities. You might want to start with simple individual exercises and build through the warm-up to team exercises of high intensity that simulate match situations.

Warm-down

A training session or match should ideally be followed by a warm-down session consisting of jogging and stretching exercises. Light recovery exercise will help to remove lactic acid more effectively from the muscles thus reducing feelings of muscular stiffness and fatigue.

Diet
and
nutrition

"In his early days at Arsenal, Tony Adams ate far too much steak and chips and junk food and his performance only improved when he switched to a diet of fish, chicken, vegetables and fruit."

Don Howe

Diet and Nutrition Conditioning

Eat, drink and be merry...unless you want to be a professional footballer. The days when players tackled a steak before a game, in the misguided belief that it would aid strength and fitness, are long gone.

Much attention is now devoted to ensuring athletes take in the right food and drink. Getting it right can make the difference between winning and losing.

Food is the body's fuel, providing the energy to allow muscles to work. Without food and drink the body cannot function. Without the right foods there is no energy. A shortage of petrol, or poor quality fuel, will leave a car either not working or at the very least working poorly, and so a lack of food or poor quality food will cause footballers to under-perform.

Some foods are harmful and should be avoided or at least taken infrequently and in small quantities.

Do:

- Cut down on fatty foods such as chips, crisps and fried foods.
- Eat less red meat, pasties, pies and sausage rolls.
- Eat carbohydrates, foods such as bread, pasta, rice, vegetables and cereals.
- Eat plenty of fruit as snacks and with meals.

Don't:

- Drink large amounts of alcohol after a game. It can lead to further dehydration when the need is to rehydrate.
- Make steak and chips your pre-match meal although grilled, lean steak with baked potatoes and salad/vegetables is fine.
- Delay the pre-match meal. It should be eaten at least 3 to 4 hours beforehand to give sufficient time for it to be digested.
- Delay the post-match meal. It should be eaten within two hours of the end of the match.
- Play on an empty stomach.

"Alcohol isn't part of their lifestyle [in Italy]. They work on the principle that your body's a machine, you drain that machine, now you've got to put back into your system whatever is good for that machine. And the one thing you don't fill it with is alcohol."

Graeme Souness

The right foods

The body's energy supply comes from the three main classes of foods – proteins, fats and carbohydrates. Fatty foods contain more energy than proteins, which in turn contain more energy than carbohydrates.

Fat is the best form of energy-containing food but only if plenty of calories of energy are required. Fatty foods contain twice as much energy as carbohydrate foods but cannot be used as an energy source during high-intensity exercise such as sprinting. Fats are only used during lower intensity aerobic exercise such as jogging. Carbohydrates can be used to fuel the muscles for prolonged aerobic activities and for sprinting. Carbohydrate-containing foods are therefore better energy-quality foods.

Proteins, found in meat, fish, dairy products and vegetables, are used as energy sources but only sparingly and usually after 45 minutes of exercise. Football falls into this category, so some attention should be given towards protein, particularly as proteins are very important for health and maintaining muscle structure. For footballers the recommendation is that they eat 1.5–2 grams (¹⁄₂₀–¹⁄₁₅ oz) of protein for each kilogram (2¼ lbs) of body weight every day. This amount of protein is generally found in a typical diet.

How much of each food type should be eaten each day?

Footballers should be eating more carbohydrates and less fats. During pre-season training and training camps the carbohydrate intake should be kept high – up to 70% of total food eaten.

The problems associated with a high fat diet:

- Too much fat is poor for general health and well-being.

- Too much fat leads to excess fat under the skin, adding to a player's percentage body fat.

- When athletes run out of stored carbohydrates in their muscles they become fatigued. Too much fat may lead to undereating carbohydrates and to a low muscle carbohydrate store.

Type of food	Typical diet for footballer	Ideal diet for footballer
Carbohydrate	46%	60%
Fat	38%	25%
Protein	16%	15%

Table 18: Typical diet showing percentages of carbohydrate, fat and protein

"I'm one of the lucky ones who can eat quite a lot and not really put weight on but I do know players who, if they look at food, put weight on. You obviously get recommended certain food that gives you strength or energy such as pasta."

Alan Shearer

Reduce fat in your diet in these ways:

- Reduce the amount of butter and margarine on sandwiches and in cooking.

- Cut down on chips, crisps and fried foods in general. Replace with boiled/baked potatoes and try grilled and steamed foods instead.

- Eat less red meat (beef, lamb and pork), pasties, pies and sausage rolls.

- Reduce the amount of sauces in cooking.

- Cut down on whole fat dairy products like milk, cheese and cream. Use low fat equivalents or substitutes instead.

"Before a match it's important to have light things, like spaghetti, rice, a lot of fruit if possible. After the game I'm very hungry so a little bit of rice with vegetables is good for me."
Winston Bogarde

The importance of carbohydrates

Research shows outfield players run about 8–13 kilometres (5–8 miles) in a game and use up large amounts (200–250 grams – 7–9 oz) of carbohydrate. These carbohydrate stores must be replaced after the match – the sooner the better.

The best time to restore carbohydrate levels into muscles is within two hours of the end of a game or training. The day of the next match is too late; there is very little that can be done at that stage to get muscle stores back to the normal levels.

Using a high carbohydrate diet it is possible to get these stores re-stocked in 24–48 hours.
About 60–70% of food eaten should come from carbohydrates. If carbohydrate intake is low then muscle stores will be low, bad news for players involved in more than one game a week or during heavy training periods. Remember, once muscle carbohydrate stores are used up the ability to sprint or run is reduced.

Carbohydrate loading

The amount of carbohydrate should be increased in the two days before a match (i.e. Thursday and Friday before a Saturday game, Monday and Tuesday before a Wednesday game).

Carbohydrates can be divided into two varieties

Simple	Complex
Sugar	Potatoes
Jam	Bread
Sweets	Pasta
Cakes	Rice
Biscuits	Vegetables
Fruit	Cereals
Soft drinks	

Simple carbohydrates have a slight advantage in helping to load the muscles in the first two hours after a match but after 24 hours there is no difference. The advantage of the complex carbohydrates is that they contain other nutrients such as minerals and vitamins not normally found in cakes and sweets (they are however found in fruit). Also simple sugars, have a higher fat content and they may be linked to an increase in coronary heart disease. Players should therefore attempt to obtain most of their carbohydrate intake via the complex variety.

A good day's diet

Breakfast: 3–4 slices of bread or toast with a little butter plus jam or marmalade. Bowl of cereal and fruit. Glass of fresh fruit juice and 1–2 cups of tea or coffee with skimmed milk.

Lunch: 4 slices of bread with fillings of tuna or chicken or turkey or egg or lean ham. Bowl of salad. 1–2 bananas, handful of raisins and an apple. Fresh fruit juice plus glass of skimmed milk. Tea or coffee.

Dinner: Large bowl of rice or pasta plus lean meat (even mince) or fish, tin of tomatoes and bowl of salad. Fruit or pudding or both. Glass of skimmed milk or fruit juice. Tea or coffee.

A diet on these lines contains little fat, enough protein and about 60% energy from carbohydrates. During intense training periods three meals a day may not be enough so 2 or 3 snacks a day should be taken from fruit, sandwiches, jam or marmalade (little or no butter/margarine), cakes, biscuits and sweets (in moderation).

"You have to look after yourself because if you don't when you get to a certain age, when you get to 30° or 40, you can't run any more and that's why I hope to get to 42, 43 and still be playing football."

Roberto Carlos

Pre-match meal

The meal before training or a match should be eaten at least 3–4 hours before, to give it sufficient time to be digested. It should be light, contain complex carbohydrates, and little fat which is difficult to digest and remains in the stomach longer than other nutrients. Grilled fish or chicken with baked or boiled potatoes and boiled/steamed vegetables or salad is ideal. Alternatively, a pasta dish with a non-fatty sauce, or baked beans or scrambled eggs on toast are suitable. Fresh fruit for a sweet, and a carbohydrate drink can also be added. You should not play on an empty stomach.

Some traditional pre-game meals such as steak and chips should be avoided because of the fat content, although, as mentioned grilled, lean steak with baked potatoes and salad/vegetables is fine.

Post-match meal

The first two hours after a game is the best time to get carbohydrates back into the muscles. Complex carbohydrates such as bread, pasta, potatoes and rice will do, as will simple carbohydrates such as cakes, puddings and sweets. Drinking carbohydrate drinks is particularly good, especially if you don't feel like eating.

Drinks

It may be difficult for players to get sufficient carbohydrates from food sources and under these circumstances a player may have to resort to carbohydrate drinks. It is also important to remember that fatigue can be caused by dehydration as well as by running out of carbohydrates. Like a car leaking water, a human body, when dehydrated due to the water loss from sweating, overheats and underperforms. Carbohydrate drinks of the right formula will get both water and carbohydrate into the body.

The well-known sports drinks – Isotar, Gatorade and Lucozade Sport – are ideal to take during exercise. Drinks such as Coca-Cola, Lucozade and Orange Barley are too carbohydrate-concentrated to be taken during exercise, but are suitable afterwards.

On average, players can lose 2–3 litres (3½–5½ pints) of sweat during a match, especially during the hot and humid conditions experienced in the last four World Cups, during pre-season training and pre- and early-season matches. Losses of 2–3 kg (4½–6½ lbs) of weight during games by English professionals have been reported, due purely and simply to not enough fluid being replaced. Scientific evidence shows that such small losses in body weight due to water loss will result in impaired and substandard performances.

"When I started out in the game, at 16 or 17, I used to have a fillet steak as pre-match meal at 12 o'clock. If you asked for that now you'd be told it was not allowed. After games there are always sandwiches and fruit in the dressing room."

Alan Shearer

How much to drink and how often?

This depends whether the drink is for consumption before, during or after the match or training session.

Before: Do not drink carbohydrate drinks in the hour or so before the start. However, you can drink five minutes or so before going onto the pitch, when it is useful to drink about 200 – 400 ml (1–2 paper cups) – especially important in hot weather.

During: Drink 200 ml (about 1 paper cup) every 20 minutes or so. Coaches should allow breaks in training every 20–30 minutes for a brief refuelling of carbohydrates and water. At half-time players are advised to drink 300–500ml (½–1 pint) of a carbohydrate-based sports drink rather than tea or water.

After: Drink as much as possible in the first 1 – 2 hours after a match/training. This is the BEST time to get carbohydrates back into the muscle. Drinks more concentrated in carbohydrates, such as Lucozade Orange Barley and other fizzy drinks are okay. You need about 100-200 grams (3½–7 fl oz) of carbohydrates in this 2 hour period. You could eat it, but remember you also need to rehydrate.

How useful is water compared with carbohydrate drinks?

This depends on the level of muscle carbohydrate stores and on the duration and intensity of the training or the game. If the muscles are well stored and you are training for up to an hour, water is probably just as good to take during training. But after training, or if training goes on past 60–90 minutes, then carbohydrate drinks will be better.

How sensible is it to have a pint or two of beer after a match?

Beer normally contains carbohydrate and some players have considered it useful to restock muscle carbohydrate stores after a match with beer. Unfortunately the amount of carbohydrate contained in beer is relatively small; you would have to drink large amounts to restock the muscle carbohydrate stores adequately.

The problem with drinking large amounts of beer is that the alcohol contains a great deal of energy which only the liver can use. The liver does not need this amount of energy so converts it into fat.

Another important point is that after a game there is a need to replace the stores of body water lost through sweating. Alcohol is a diuretic, and so makes a person want to urinate. This could lead to further dehydration.

To sum up, drink and eat carbohydrate-containing foods in the first hour or two after a game, then enjoy a beer or two in moderation!

"If you ask the professionals now, with the amount of football they play, they have to look after themselves. I have plenty of rest, eat the proper foods, don't have many late nights."

Steve McManaman

Mental **preparation** *for* performance

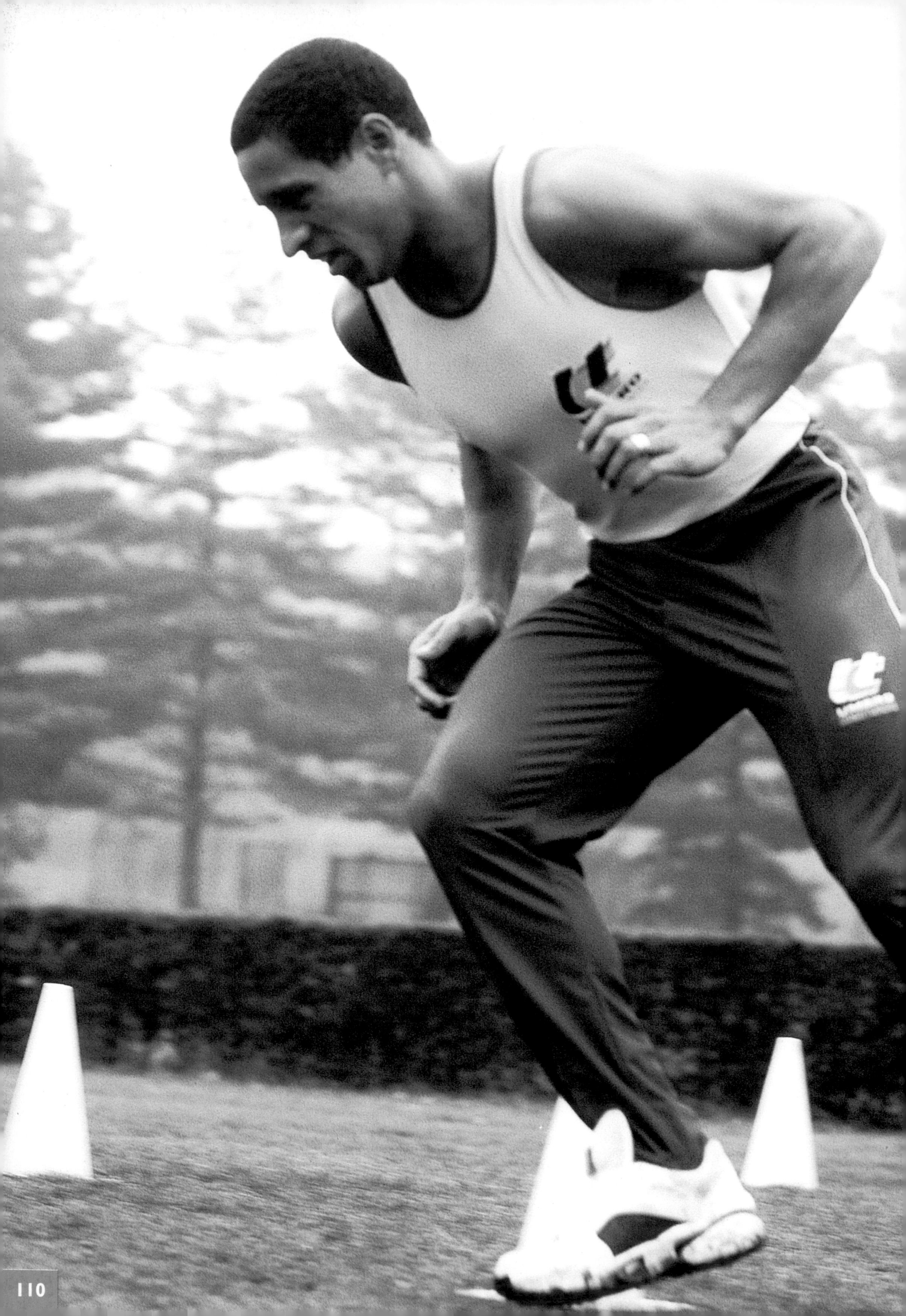

It's always been called the beautiful game. In the modern era, it's increasingly becoming the mind game.

Alan Shearer's breathtaking bursts of pace in the last quarter of the field make him the great predator of the modern European game. But it is often not just sheer fitness that gives Shearer a yard on most defenders. With the right mental fine-tuning before and during the game, he will know when exactly to start a run and exactly where to take it.

As British athletics coach Frank Dick put it, shortly before the 100 metre sprint final at the Barcelona Olympics:

"It is mental power that separates the exceptional from the very good. When they line up for the race there will be nothing to choose between them, talent for talent, training for training. What separates them is what goes on behind the eyes."

Frank Dick

Wimbledon midfielder Vinny Jones is famous for "psyching" himself and his team-mates up before a game with loud rap music in the changing room and loud taunts at the opposition in the tunnel. Some Liverpool players to this day say Wimbledon's crude tactics played a crucial part in their 1989 FA Cup Final win over the Reds. Even Nottingham Forest defender Stuart Pearce, one of football's most respected figures, says high decibel blasts of punk rock music on his personal stereo help put him in the right mood for a contest.

The point about good mental preparation is that it gives and maintains a high state of confidence. The most gifted players in the world can be snuffed out of a game if their confidence is hit – say by an early

"Confidence plays a big part, and if your confidence is sky high then things will automatically happen, i.e. goals will go in and you'll make the right pass. If the confidence is low you won't possibly shoot when you should, you won't cross when you should, you might not tackle or pass when you should."

Alan Shearer

crunching tackle – and they do not have the strength of mind to deal with it, think of the next task ahead, and move on.

Imagery is the technical term for a technique that can tune an athlete's mental preparation. It means creating an image in the player's mind of the game ahead - a way of "seeing" and "feeling" the action by simply thinking about it. Sports scientists have discovered that imagery cannot only help prepare a player for competition, but also improve the technical abilities and the desire to train and practise.

Beginners often confuse imagery with day-dreaming, or even the dreams we have in sleep, because they appear similar. But the crucial difference is that dreaming is always random and uncontrollable.

"You have to relax as much as possible." Roberto Carlos

With imagery, players use their imaginations at set times of the day, it is more controlled and constructive than day-dreaming, and may focus set parts of the game (such as passing, running off the ball or accurate crossing). This exercise is more like virtual reality than day-dreaming, except there are no high-tech headsets to help you achieve your aim. There are two ways of approaching it:

- *External imagery:* This is when the player thinks about the game as if they were watching a video of themselves on the pitch.

- *Internal imagery:* This is when the player thinks about the game as if they were actually playing it – through their own eyes.

"Before the match, there's the concentration, and within this concentration, you think about what you are going to do during the match. In order to know what's going to happen in the game, you have to imagine it beforehand."

Roberto Carlos

Learning to use imagery

Like any other skill, practice makes perfect. Sports scientists recommend short, sharp bursts – for instance three sessions a day lasting only five to ten minutes. Here is a step-by-step guide to getting your imagery programme up and running.

Imagery exercises

In these exercises, players focus their minds on objects and details.

Exercise one

1. Find a quiet room where you will not be disturbed.

2. Place a football in front of you where you can clearly see it.

3. Sit in a comfortable chair and relax.

4. Look hard at the ball and think hard about its many features.

5. Close your eyes and try to get a clear image of the ball in your mind.

6. Look at the ball in your image and identify those same features.

Work on this exercise and try and create a clear, vivid image.

This simple exercise can be repeated with the emphasis on touch, simply by holding the ball and using your hands to trace its features.

In this excercise you try to see and *feel* your hands moving over the ball. Again practice this and try to improve both the visual image and the sense of touch.

Exercise two

Now you are ready to try out your imagination on a football scene, such as a stadium. To help you concentrate on the overall sights and smells of a football ground, think of it as still (as it would be before the players run out).

1. Find a quiet space where you will not be disturbed.

2. Sit relaxed in a comfortable chair.

3. Close your eyes and focus on your breathing - deeply in through your nose and out through your mouth.

4. Imagine the stadium, in which you are standing.

5. Focus on what you can see, looking straight ahead and at either side.

6. Note the visual scene, then open your eyes.

7. Repeat the process, this time noting the smells.

Exercise three

For the next practice, the scene around you will be moving, while you remain quite still. Now you are moving on to imagining the preparation and actual action of the game.

Follow steps 1–3 of exercise two, then:

1. Imagine the scene.

2. Look around, noticing what you see and how you feel.

3. Concentrate on any thoughts and sounds (for action).

4. Focus on the movements of the imaginary players.

5. Try to capture the sounds of the game.

6. Open your eyes when the sequence is completed.

Next, repeat all the steps and try to imagine the sounds of the moving players on the pitch. Then go all the way through from numbers one to six, trying to bring the sights and sounds together. The more you practice the more likely that the image will seem lifelike and real.

"I think you've got to relax, just try to think about what you'll try to do in the game. You'll think possibly about corners that have been worked on in the week before a match, or free kicks, or whatever. You'll think about what your job is – defending corners, attacking corners, throw-ins, just little things like that."

Alan Shearer

Exercise four

Now you are ready to imagine a scene in which you are actually one of the players. Again you will be preparing the action, then starting the play.

Follow the steps 1–3 of exercise two, then:

1. Imagine the stadium in which you are playing and focus on how it feels.

2. Focus on what you see and what you can hear (for action).

3. When the game begins, sense how this feels and sounds.

4. Concentrate on any thoughts, particularly the feeling of movement.

Exercise five

This uses imagery to improve your technical skills. Now you can concentrate on a particular move, such as a penalty kick or cross from the wings. For this you can try to create an imagery script – literally a list of directions compiled by you. The more detailed the script is, the more lifelike the imagery practice will be. So your script has to include details like the position of the players, the direction of the wind, the feel of the boot studs on the pitch and the sound of the crowd. Even elements as focussed as your heart rate and muscle movements and the direction of spin on the ball should be included. Here's an example of an imagery script, in this case for crossing the ball at pace from the wing. The simple idea is that if you can perfect this move in your imagination and you practice the move on the training pitch, then you have a very good chance of perfecting it for use in competition.

1. I see the defender trying to force me in-field.

2. I hear the centre forward shout "take him on".

3. I see the ball at my feet, my knee over the ball.

4. I feel my shoulder dip as I feint to go inside, at the same time my left foot pushes the ball forward.

5. I drive hard with my right leg, feel the ground under my boot, my arms drive (as I accelerate after the ball).

6. I think "cross the ball with pace".

7. I glance into the penalty area and see the centre forward peeling away towards the far post.

8. I switch focus on to the ball.

9. I adjust my stride and feel my legs hit the tempo and rhythm.

10. I feel my body lean away and whip my left foot around the ball.

11. I feel my body overbalance as I watch the ball arc into the penalty box.

Imagery scripts and changes in technical execution

When practising techniques, players are likely to seek out advice from coaches and other players. This may result in a player refining the way a technique is executed. Any slight changes in technique will be accompanied by alterations in how it "feels". As an example, when crossing from a wide position, a player may be reckoned to be too close to the ball as they shape up to hit the centre. A coach or team-mate might advise a change, such as attempting to strike the ball when it is a little further away from the body. This adjustment will result in the technique "feeling" very different, and will alter the way a player sees the ball, the way they organize their stride pattern before the strike and the body position on impact.

Only when this new approach has been tried, and the player becomes aware of how it feels, should it be translated into the imagery script.

Imagery scripts tend to become increasingly detailed as players focus on adjusting small aspects of their technique. As with goal-setting, it can be helpful if someone assists a player who wishes to use imagery to help them develop the technical aspects of their game. And that doesn't necessarily mean employing a coach. Teachers, parents and team-mates can all share their knowledge, give advice and help players become better in a technical sense.

The key to a good imagery session of this kind is that it is imagined in "real time" (i.e. not in slow motion), that it is a realistic movement (i.e. not an overhead kicked goal from inside your own penalty area) and that it has a positive result (i.e. the pass reaches your team-mate). Success, even though it is imagined, can lead to greater confidence. And greater confidence must inevitably lead to better performance.

Imagery as part of a pre-match plan:

High-performance athletes from all sport are well known for approaching competition in a positive manner. The successful ones tend to be fully confident in their ability to cope with the task ahead and free from any self-doubt or damaging thoughts of defeat. This is an excellent way for footballers to feel as they prepare to compete.

A player's sense of self-belief often stems from the simple knowledge that they have worked hard at their game. Years of hard training and success on the field bring a sense of self-assurance. But self-confidence alone does not guarantee a player will start a match in the right frame of mind. Players who are properly focused at kick-off are the ones who are likely to have followed a structured pre-match plan.

Imagery can be used to:

- Create a state of mental readiness.

- Focus attention on key aspects of the performance ahead.

- Enhance self-confidence.

The manager's team talk is obviously a vital part of the plan, but it is also important for the individual players to be in control. For example, they might have set times for physical, flexibility exercises, and set times for technical and mental preparation. Here we can see how imagery can help with the mental side of the game.

Pre-match readiness will mean different things to different players. Some, like Bobby Moore and Gary Lineker, liked to start matches in a calm, controlled state. Others like to increase their aggression and excitement by pumping up the adrenalin.

Even Alan Shearer, known as one of the most level-headed men in the game, admits of his own pre-match preparation:

> *"Oh, I'll shout and things."*　Alan Shearer

As players become more experienced they usually learn to understand how they need to feel before a match. Imagery has a role to play here as it can have both a calming and activating effect.

Because imagery takes place in the player's head, it is a portable tool that can be employed anywhere, any time. For example, it can be used in the changing room, during a pitch inspection, or during breaks in physical exercise. It can remind players of what they intend to do during play, and be used to reinforce their competition aims. Player's can think about or verbalize their personal goals and use imagery to see and feel them being executed. Self-confidence can be boosted by using imagery to replay positive examples of past play.

Sometimes before a match players may feel lethargic or distracted, by the opposition or by the crowd. The use of imagery helps them to regain a sense of purpose.

Imagery can also be used in tandem with positive self-statements. For example, if a player is concentrating on his ability to jump and head for goal, the thought can be accompanied by the repeated words "I will score" or "I will beat the defender", either spoken quietly or out loud. The positive self-statement may sound a little like an off-the-wall idea – but not if it works for you!

The example on page 124 illustrates how imagery and self-statements might feature in a pre-match routine, highlighting three different occasions – the morning of the match, arriving at the venue, and the final 15 minutes before kick-off. In this example, the self-statements support the mental image of good passing. The simple aim is to make the player believe that he/she has the ability to perform that skill in open play.

Note: In this example, the mental and verbal combination is used quite late in the cycle. In fact, players can use imagery and self-statements at any time.

Pre-match Routine

On the morning of the match:

Ten minutes of imagery at home using scripts that cover tackling, crossing the ball and passing accurately out of defence. After reading each script the player relaxes by breathing in and out slowly for five breaths, closing the eyes and engaging the image. Each image should be repeated three times.

Arriving at the venue:

Imagery is used while the player is inspecting the pitch. The player looks around the stadium, stretches the limbs and begins to focus on his/her aims for the game. The player thinks about the importance of passing the ball well, breathes easily, then engages imagery of good passing.

Fifteen minutes before kick-off:

- Imagery used briefly between warming up exercises. The player thinks about the process of winning the ball, talking to team-mates and good passing. The player verbalizes the aim out loud, then engages a matching image.

- The player adds a positive self-statement, such as "Good tackle, good pass".

- The player thinks "Pass to feet, always quality".

- Imagery of excellent passing used.

- Another positive self-statement, such as "It's easy, we will win".

Liverpool's Steve McManaman already uses his own form of imagery before every game.

In his own way, Steve is playing mind games to maximize the physical strengths and skills he works on in training. With talents like his, Steve doesn't really have to worry too much about the technical side of his game. But he proves the simple point, made earlier by athletics coach Frank Dick, that the difference between the exceptional and the very good is "what goes on behind the eyes". And what goes on behind the eyes is what imagery seeks to control.

"While other team-mates may be working out or taking a bath, I always like to walk around outside the changing room, getting a bit of fresh air and focusing on the game."

Steve McManaman

Index